Layout and graphics by Nicoletta Azzolini
Some of the design are by Freepik, Vecteezy, and Brgfx (via Freepik). Icons via Flaticon by Tomas Knop, Smashicons, and Freepik)

Index by Georgina Bomer

ISBN: 978-0-692-08858-6

Colleen Beck, OTR/L

The Sensory Lifestyle Handbook

How to Create Meaningful and Motivating Sensory Enrichment for Sensory-Filled Days

www.theottoolbox.com

Contents

For the child with sensory processing issues, the monotony of the daily grind is anything but repetitious.

Sensory processing challenges can arise with every breath, every falling leaf, and every dust particle. When everyday details end in meltdowns, panic attacks, screaming fits, and complete meltdowns, the child with these daily struggles is understandably at their wit's end. It is agonizing to be an individual who cannot perceive their environment without system failure. It can be frustrating and exhausting to parent or teach a child whose sensory systems are so out of whack that daily tasks seem like a marathon of overwhelming feelings.

Often times, parents of these children have researched every option, fought for every accommodation, and tried every tactic, only to continue seeking answers.

This book is a strategy guide for sensory processing needs. It's a system of interpreting information in order to guide therapeutic tactics. It's a resource on using sensory diets as a lifestyle change. This book helps assess the outcomes of sensory input and intervention strategies in order to improve integration of the sensory systems. This book provides strategies to support and challenge the sensory systems through deep and meaningful interventions so that a lifestyle change enables modulation and regulation of sensation.

All of us experience challenges to our sensory systems. Consider holiday shopping in a crowded mall an hour after your usual lunch time. Sensory input flies in from every direction. Add heavy winter coats, crowded shops, frazzled nerves, hunger, and the stress of a limited budget. At some point, the system has to break and we can no longer integrate all of those senses. We fall apart. We drop the unpurchased items and hightail it out of the mall into the cool open expanse of the (overcrowded, yet cool) parking lot. We have a tendency to respond to the stress with anxiety, depression, or other meltdowns. As adults who know that time of year is coming each calendar year, we use compensatory strategies or modulation strategies that we have developed over time. Shopping trips are then done in shorter trips, and we bring items like a water bottle and comfortable clothing. We've learned over time, the strategies to compensate for sensory overload.

Children are not developmentally capable of applying these strategies to their own sensory challenge. And for the child who inaccurately perceives or processes sensory information, it's

a recipe for meltdowns, panic attacks, crying fits, physical outbursts, or other mechanisms of response.

The child with sensory processing challenges, who is unable to identify these unspoken sensory needs will typically show resulting behaviors. One strategy to help is an outline of specific sensory input designed to meet the needs of the individual: The Sensory Diet.

Direct therapeutic intervention is the key ingredient in the process of improving functional independence across environments. However, the implementation of an individualized sensory diet that regularly addresses the child's sensory processing needs throughout the day is effective. A child is able to participate more appropriately in daily activities when benefiting from sensory input that has been provided at frequent and expected intervals. Implementation of a special diet of sensory input should involve all aspects of the individual's day so that the "sensory diet" looks more like a sensory lifestyle rather than a prescribed intervention.

The sensory integration principles and activities that make up a sensory diet are considered acceptable treatment of underlying needs and are a part of a recommended course of action.

This book was designed after many requests for specific activities that would meet the needs of children with sensory issues. The highly motivating sensory activities outlined in this collection are ones that are designed to meet sensory needs and establish a point of reference for functional participation in daily tasks.

This sensory diet book is divided into several sections. First is an explanation of sensory diets and a description of special interest sensory diets that can be integrated into the life of a child with sensory processing needs. A section under warnings will provide considerations that should always be exercised with set-up and continual use of a sensory diet. Next, is an explanation of the sensory systems and a breakdown of calming and alerting sensory activities. You will then find themed activities that are designed to promote sensory participation and challenge each individual sensory system. These activities may be used in a sensory diet as a motivating tool for providing sensory input. Activities can be combined in myriad ways to provide ongoing therapeutic tools to challenge the sensory systems while promoting attention, focus, behaviors, social interactions, and development. The last section of this book provides themed sensory diet schedule tools, goal sheets, behavioral charts, data sheets, and sensory diet implementation tools.

For most, the ability interpret incoming sensory information occurs in a reactive and appropriate manner. Individuals with sensory processing issues have difficulty with many areas of regulating sensory input. As a result, sensory information is often times overwhelming or lacking in intensity for these individuals. Depending on an individual's integration of this process sensory information, resulting behaviors can impact a person's ability to function. Sensory information from the environment is accepted, interpreted, accommodated for, and processed to result in meaningful, appropriate, and functional behaviors.

Importantly, the child with or without sensory

processing issues needs to participate in occupations. From play and self-care to meal time and interacting in the community, the strategies of a sensory diet need to be appropriate for a variety of situations. There may be sensory diet techniques that are used on specific days or before specific experiences that are not used on other occasions or like the strategies that are used on a daily basis. All of this is part of the experiment of finding the "just right" sensory diet, evaluating responsiveness, and adjusting as needed.

When a person with sensory processing difficulties struggles in one or more of these steps, sensory output is impacted. It is here that behaviors and tendencies to accommodate for the impaired sensory system result in meltdowns, overwhelming responses to sensory input, stress, and a breakdown in functional skills. It can be very difficult to pin point the breakdown in the sensory system. Individuals who have lived with this processing system their whole lives may not know that sensory input or sensory needs should not cause stress and struggle. Just like the person who puts on a pair of glasses for the first time can suddenly see the blurriness they experienced before, the person with sensory

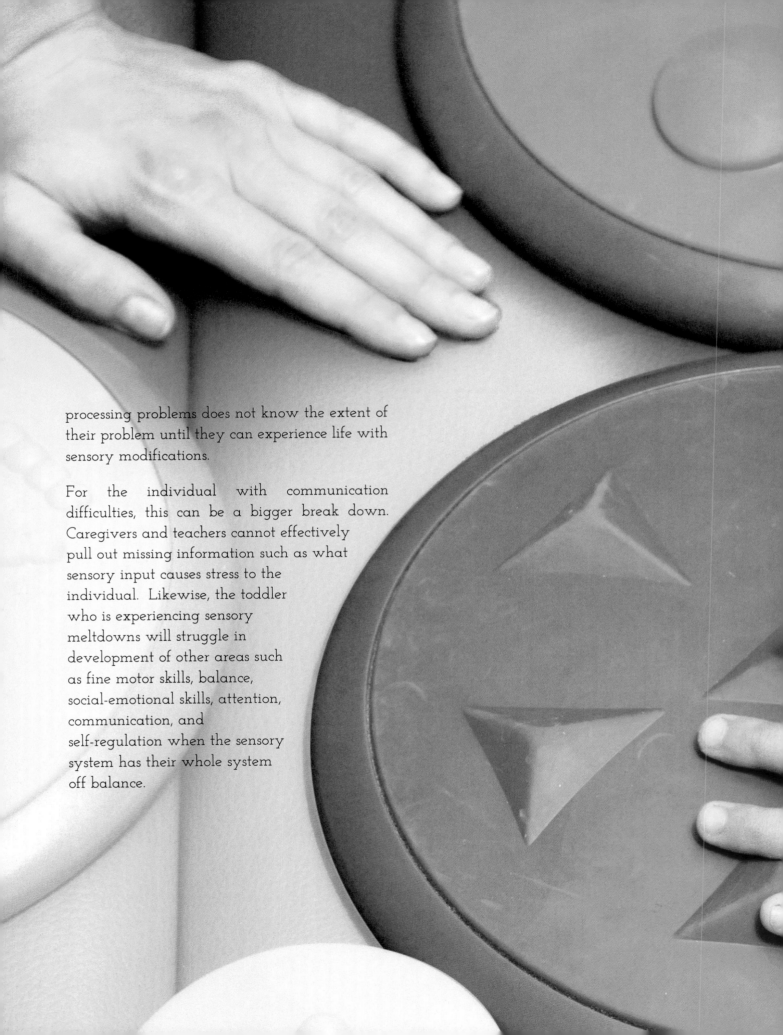

processing problems does not know the extent of their problem until they can experience life with sensory modifications.

For the individual with communication difficulties, this can be a bigger break down. Caregivers and teachers cannot effectively pull out missing information such as what sensory input causes stress to the individual. Likewise, the toddler who is experiencing sensory meltdowns will struggle in development of other areas such as fine motor skills, balance, social-emotional skills, attention, communication, and self-regulation when the sensory system has their whole system off balance.

Disclaimer

When talking to therapists, you will find a general understanding and instruction: Every child is different and every child's needs are different. There is no child that will respond exactly like another when it comes to sensory interventions and strategies. Strategies that are implemented into sensory diets need to be at the determination by an occupational therapist who has assessed or intervened while determining the child's individual needs.

A calming activity may not be calming to every child. A calming activity may not calm in every instance. Our children like to keep us on our toes! And those with sensory needs are no exception. But there is more to the differences in preferences and sensory needs. There can be harm done by inaccuracies in type of sensory input.

The occupational therapist's role in the development of the sensory diet is essential for safe and effective means for intervention and integration of sensory input. Therapists can provide information regarding the "why" and how of the sensory systems. This background understanding is a helpful tool in understanding a child's behaviors and sensory system.

Information in this book is not to be construed as professional advice or medical recommendations. It is not intended to be a substitute for informed medical advice or care. You should not use this information to diagnose or treat any health problems or illnesses without consulting your family doctor. You should not use this information as self-diagnosis or for treating a health problem or disease.

Readers should direct any questions concerning personal health care to licensed physicians, Occupational Therapists, and through individualized evaluation and intervention.

The author of this book shall not be liable, under any circumstances, for any claim, expense, damage or loss of any kind, including but not limited to, any direct, indirect, incidental, special, consequential, or punitive damages that result from your use, misuse, or inability to use this book. You agree to indemnify and hold harmless the author of this book and any of its affiliates and business partners from any liability whatsoever, including but not limited to damage to intellectual property rights arising from the alteration, publication, downloading, uploading, use or misuse of the information contained on this book.

Chapter 1
Sensory and The Whole Child

You may have said it before

* My child jumps and crashes on the couch all the time!

* My child refuses to wear socks. It's a daily battle.

* My child chews her shirt so much that it's soaking wet.

* My student gets so overwhelmed by his emotions and breaks down daily.

* My child won't wear pants, even when it's freezing cold outside.

* My child HATES the sound of the vacuum. I need to wait until he is out of the house to clean.

* My students can't focus! They won't STOP moving.

* My client thrives in therapy sessions but he struggles at home or school.

All of these comments have one thing in common: A sensory need is not being met. Underlying areas of the sensory processing system are being challenged.

One way that the sensory system can be integrated to produce functional results (aka

wearing socks; regulating emotions; stopping to focus and listen) is a tool called the sensory diet.

A sensory diet can be used to provide the sensory input needed to meet these needs in order to integrate their sensory systems in a functional manner. Once sensory-related behaviors and antecedents are determined, the particulars of a child's sensory needs can be met with a specific sensory diet.

Sensory Diet Strategies Can Look Like...

Allow the child who jumps and crashes all over the house to have a fifteen-minute jump break on a mini-trampoline. Then add a little heavy work by playing hopscotch while completing spelling words.

Allow the child who chews on their shirt to eat a snack of homemade fruit leather. Provide them with a chew bracelet during school or on the bus ride.

For the child who won't wear pants, try leg exercises with a therapy band followed by rubbing thick lotion on the legs.

Allow the child who can't stand the sound of the vacuum to listen to music with headphones in a cozy corner of the home while the vacuum is running.

Each of these strategies may work to improve independence and function in one child but not for another. One child may require more force, more resistance, more vestibular input, or more visual input. Another child may respond well in one instance but not another.

As you can see, observation and data collection in the development of a sensory diet is extremely important in promoting function and independence of a fully integrated sensory system. The child's behaviors are a clue to a hidden problem. Behavioral responses are a means of communication used by the child's body and sensory system. That information is used to determine what the child needs.

Observation is very important. What works for one child on one particular day given specific experiences, emotions, environment, and supports (or lack of supports) will not work for another child with similar experiences. Even a child who has sensory diet that seems to work in one particular moment can present differently the next day. A sensory diet is about discovering strategies that can be incorporated into a lifestyle.

Once the observation piece is determined in the child with sensory needs, it's important to keep going! Observe, observe, and observe the child some more. A therapist should perform a comprehensive evaluation (and do more observing!) before recommending activities that meet the sensory needs of the child. Once sensory strategies are determined and trialed, even more observation should occur. Sensory input can result in sensory behaviors that are

different for each child. Especially in the initial stages of implementing sensory strategies, it is so important to note type, frequency, environment, and response of sensory input.

When a sensory diet is implemented, there will be changes in the child's behaviors and responses. These changes can be minute or they can be vast. Each should be monitored and documented. A Sensory Diet is a tool that has immense capability for positive changes in the life of a child and the child's experiences at home, school, and in the community. As a result, the life around that child, including those in the classroom, family members will be significantly impacted as well.

NOTE: It is possible for the beginning stages of a Sensory Diet to result in adverse behaviors or impaired functioning. Changes in behavior, both positive and negative should be relayed and communicated with the child's therapist as a more effective strategy is trialed.

A few important reminders about Sensory Diets:

✱ Remember that the home program portion of a Sensory Diet is extremely important.

✱ The monitoring and observation of Sensory Diet strategies are a must.

✱ Sensory Diets should be positive experiences for the child, and never presented in a negative manner.

✱ Sensory Diet strategies should be motivating for the child's interests and values.

✳ Sensory Diet activities should involve a choice for the child.

The Puzzle of Puzzles

If you are reading this book, it probably means you know or love a child with sensory needs. You might be a parent, grandparent, guardian, teacher, therapist, counselor, school administrator, caregiver, or other person who is involved with a child whose sensory challenges interfere with daily tasks.

You might see that child in the classroom where they jump up from their seat and bump into their peers while humming or slapping the desk. You might know that child since they were an infant and could see their daily struggle in every task.   You might be trying to help that child meet their sensory needs across many contexts and know that there seems to be something "off". Whatever your role is to that child, there is one single thing in common. You have a deep desire to help that individual live their life without unnecessary struggle.

Now let's shift the thinking from the role you're playing and the environment that you are viewing this child's abilities.   From the child's point of view, they see and know many different helpers in their day. But what are these helper people trying to do?   They encourage learning. They help them walk from classroom to classroom during the school day. They make their meals and tell them when to sleep, bathe, get dressed, eat, and turn off the tablet. Helper people can seem pretty bossy!

For the child with sensory processing challenges, moving from activity to activity or throughout the parts of the day can be a struggle when it comes to allowing their body and mind to catch up to the schedule of the day. A guide or visual that helps the child know what they can expect can help.

Every one of us has a sensory diet. Some start the day with a hot cup of coffee. Others relax at the end of the day under a warm and cozy blanket with a good book. Others start their day with a vegetable smoothie or crunchy granola. Then there are the sensory tasks that meet underlying needs. During the day, we stretch; we yawn; we doodle; we get up and move during a long work day in front of a computer screen; we jiggle our legs during a boring meeting; we tap our fingers on the steering wheel during traffic. Each of these actions provides sensory input in a manner that integrates our sensory systems into the input from the world around us.

Consider the sensory components that make up our days. The warm ceramic coffee mug touches your hands as you slowly sip a slop drink of coffee. It's a very calming experience. These daily doses of sensory input are integrated and we are able to function.

When we consider the sensory tasks that are interfering with a child's ability to function and self-regulate, adaptations can be made.

All of these pieces make up the puzzle that is a sensory diet. The activities, tools, and adjustments that allow an individual to get through a day can be a true puzzle when it comes to figuring out what works and what doesn't work.

Finding the "just right" state using sensory strategies takes time. It is a puzzle that is constantly evolving. That puzzle isn't just your run-of-the-mill 500-piece table puzzle with shapes and colors for clues. It's a three-dimensional puzzle that changes perhaps on a daily basis. It's a puzzle of puzzles.

How can this puzzle ever be solved? It needs to be a constantly evolving system of assessment, goal monitoring, and adjustments. This book will help you on your way to solving that Rubik cube.

It can be very confusing when trying to figure out where to begin when it comes to addressing sensory needs. Many times, the confusion and frustration start long before a diagnosis or even thoughts of seeking professional help. That gut feeling that something is "off" is usually the first sign of sensory issues. Luckily, there is an abundance of information related to sensory processing available in books and online. Help is becoming more readily available. A re-occurring theme in this book will be the push to seek professional help. Whether you are uncertain of a diagnosis or a treatment strategy, seek out the proper diagnosis and appropriate treatment. This is an issue of safety and development, and is extremely important.

The Whole Child

When we see a child, we need to look at the whole child. Addressing the individual components of the sensory system are important, but the trick to beginning to solve that puzzle of puzzles that makes up the child with sensory processing challenges is looking at the whole child.

The whole child concept is the "big picture". The Ecology of Human Performance (Dunn, Brown, & McGuire, 1994) describes the understanding of the child within a context. Within that context is an intervention that encompasses the child as a participant and which is used to established to accomplish a particular goal. For example, within the context of the school classroom, the child has an occupation as a student. The interventions are established within the context in order to address specific needs such as attention, sensory regulation, handwriting, fine motor skills, etc. The child is surrounded by the intervention in order to be successful within the context of the school.

Rather than addressing the parts of the sensory system in isolation, consider thinking about the big picture.

Context of the Child- The context of a child encompasses the child's occupation. Examples of context include the environment, home, school, a grandparent's house, child care, etc.

The Occupation of the Child- Performance patterns that make up the individual include habits, routines, patterns, and roles. These components will be vastly different from one

individual to another.

The one basic and primary occupation of every child is that of play. As the child's primary occupation, play is a vessel for propelling development. Development of cognition, motor skills, executive functioning levels, sensory tolerance and understanding, language, and social-emotional skills happen naturally and sequentially through play.

Utilizing this primary occupation as a tool for incorporating sensory strategies to meet the integration needs of a child is powerful. You will read more about merging a sensory diet into the occupation of play and individualized special interests later in this book.

The Environment of the Child- Environmental components include the family, parenting, emotional wellbeing, physical wellbeing, and family interaction. Each of these areas can be fluid in state, meaning that components of the environment can change vastly from one day to the next, but overall wellbeing and family states are typically static in nature. The smallest disruption such as a breakout of the flu in a family can have a huge impact on the child with sensory processing needs.

The Child- Individually, the person is challenged by behaviors, developmental considerations, and sensory integration. These considerations make a vast impression on overall functioning.

Taking all of these pieces into consideration, can we look at what the child is being asked to do during their day, how the child reacts to changes, the support system in place, the development and behaviors of the child, and all of the other areas? How is the child able to use his or her strengths to function and self-regulate? What areas cause an area of weakness in an individual?

Later in this book, you will find information on creating sensory diets specific to the context and environment of a child. Looking at these components as a part of the whole child and creating context-centered sensory diets ensures strategies are authentic and motivating.

Chapter 2
The Sensory System Puzzle

"Sensory diet" is a term that is frequently used. It is a concept that is introduced and used in many homes, classrooms, and therapy clinics to meet sensory needs. A parent looking a set of sensory tools for a child with sensory needs can use a sensory diet. A teacher of a child who is struggling in the classroom can use a sensory diet to meet regulation needs. A parent of a child with sensory-related behaviors that are out of control can use a sensory diet. In general, difficulties with regulating sensory information, regulation of emotions, and regulation of responses indicate a need for a sensory diet.

The constant balancing of the sympathetic and the parasympathetic nervous is necessary for interaction with the environment. Many times, students need to move in order to regulate their systems for optimal learning. Every individual needs to self-regulate in order to respond to the environment's challenges. Using multiple modes of sensory strategies can enhance participation.

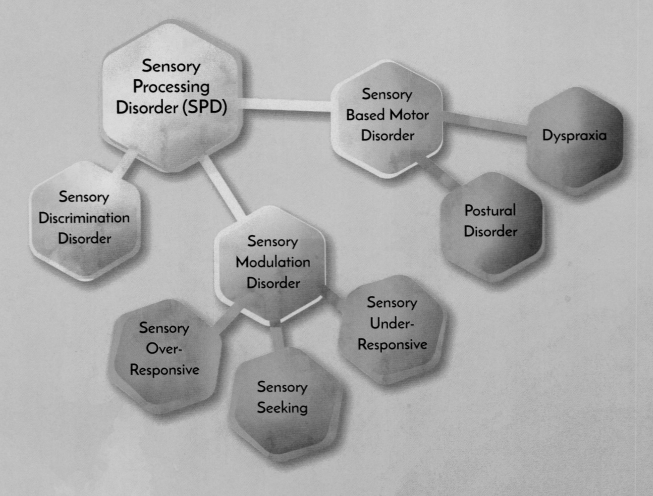

First, let's talk about types of sensory processing disorders:

Sensory processing disorder- Read more about this below.

Sensory modulation disorder- These kids have problems regulating response to sensory input. With these children, you will see a withdrawal of responses. They will become upset by noises and sounds and are easily distracted by stimuli. These children commonly fall under three categories: Sensory Over-Responsiveness, Sensory Under-Responsiveness, and Sensory Seeking. These subcategories are explained in further detail under the sensory systems section. For children who struggle in this area, a sensory diet might help them to modulate sensation in the environment. Children experience a poor compatibility of sensory information and the tasks they need to accomplish.

Sensory discrimination disorders - Children with this difficulty have problems recognizing or interpreting differences in stimuli. They will bump and crash into others or objects. These children drop items, have poor balance, and are overly afraid of heights or balance challenges.

Sensory Based Motor Disorder- These children have difficulty navigating their world. Their bodies don't do what their brains tell them to do. Sensory Based Motor Disorder has two subcategories: Dyspraxia and Postural Disorder.

1.) Dyspraxia - Children with dyspraxia have difficulty planning, timing, organizing, sequencing, or executing unfamiliar actions. These children may appear awkward and poorly coordinated. Dyspraxia describes developmentally acquired motor planning deficits and includes poor planning of movements.

2.) Postural-Ocular disorder - Children with postural-ocular disorder have trouble with controlling movements and posture. They may have difficulty with coordination of functional vision. Joint instability seen in these children results in controlled motions. These children may slouch in their seats and exhibit muscle weakness, low tone, or poor balance. Kids with postural disorders have difficulty keeping up with their peers and may appear as lazy or clumsy.

Additional considerations

Emotional regulation - Children with this difficulty have trouble maintaining an emotional state that matches the task or activity. They may overrespond to emotional situations.

Somatodyspraxia is a type of sensory-integrative based dyspraxia where there is evidence of poor processing of somatosensory information. Essentially, somatodyspraxia is a combination of visual and proprioceptive input. The somatosensory system interprets information from the skin and around joints and carries that information to the central nervous system. This includes tactile discrimination vibration, touch-pressure, proprioception, position of body in space. All of this information leads to one's ability to perceive temporal and spatial organization, develop body scheme and postural response, stabilize the head and body during movement, and interpret touch sensation and pain needed for movements and actions.

Children with somatodyspraxia often exhibit poor tactile and proprioceptive processing, clumsiness, frequent tripping, falling, and bumping into objects; difficulty with fine motor and manipulation skills, and poor organization (Cermak, 1991). Treatment focuses on providing heavy work, deep pressure, and light-touch experiences. Verbal cuing and feedback may also be used (Koomar & Bundy, 1991). The sensory diet and environmental modification ideas for decreased discrimination of tactile and proprioceptive information should be used in addition to the ideas specific to praxis issues.

Impaired Bilateral Motor Coordination

Children with impaired bilateral motor coordination often exhibit difficulty with bilateral activities, or tasks that require the two sides of the body to work together in a coordinated manner. This includes clapping, hopping, skipping, and jumping jacks. These children may have some right-left confusion, avoid midline crossing, and have difficulty developing a hand preference. Additionally, they appear to have vestibular and proprioceptive difficulties. Treatment generally focuses on providing vestibular and proprioceptive experiences and graded bilateral activities. Treatment may start with simple crossing midline, rotation, and symmetrical activities and work toward asymmetrical activities and more complex coordination skills (Koomar & Bundy, 1991). The sensory diet and environmental modification ideas for decreased discrimination of vestibular and proprioceptive information that address vestibular input should be used in addition to the ideas specific to bilateral

motor coordination.

Tactile Defensiveness

Children with tactile defensiveness often exhibit an aversive response to a variety of tactile experiences, such as craft materials, food, clothing, bathing, or touch. They will often avoid a variety of activities and may react aggressively at times. They can be easily distracted and have difficulty with attention. Therapy generally focuses on providing heavy work and deep pressure input. Slow linear vestibular input may also be helpful. Therapy also provides opportunities for participation in graded tactile experiences (Royeen & Lane, 1991). The proprioceptive sensory diet ideas for decreased discrimination of proprioceptive and vestibular information could be used in addition to the ideas specific to tactile defensiveness.

Gravitational Insecurity

Children with gravitational insecurity may exhibit limited participation in gross motor play; avoidance or fear of escalators, elevators, cars, or planes; or resistance to being off the ground. Treatment in the clinic environment generally focuses on providing proprioceptive input and graded vestibular input. In treatment, the child is always in control of the amount of vestibular input received and is never pushed beyond his or her limits (Koomar & Bundy, 1991). Environmental modifications would focus on helping the child to feel safe in all environments and situations. Sensory diet activities would focus on providing calming proprioceptive input throughout the day. The proprioceptive sensory diet ideas for decreased discrimination of proprioceptive and vestibular information could be used in addition

to the ideas specific to gravitational insecurity.

Individuals with these difficulties may have certain behaviors or characteristics in common. There are underlying needs that result in adverse reactions to sensory processing. The integration of sensory input leads to poor attention, regulation, self-monitoring, self-esteem, anxiety, discrimination, motor skills, communication, or responsiveness. Incorporating healthy sensory habits within the family lifestyle is critical to success.

The Sensory Systems

Most of us learn about the five senses early in our childhood education. Taste, touch, sight, sound, and scent are ingrained from a very young age. It might be surprising to find out there are actually more than just five sensory systems. With a typical Google search, you will learn that there are two more sensory systems that are added on to those five sensory systems. The **proprioception system** and **vestibular system** are two additional sensory systems. However, when we consider perception, regulation, movement, interaction, and functioning, there are actually MORE systems that are involved. These important systems are deeply connected to the central nervous system and are essential for perceiving and interpreting our world around us. While they do not specifically sense input from the environment, they are and always have been an essential part of our existence.

Interoception is the sensory system of our inner body. It includes organs, our heart, blood vessels, etc. While the receptors to the five commonly known senses are obvious and clear, the receptors to the interoceptive system are inside our bodies. They may not be seen but they are definitely important for functions such as emotional awareness, hunger, nervousness, fear, and feelings. Our ability to sense fullness, elimination needs, temperature, thirst, sweat, and all require regulation of the interception system.

You can see how this system is very much related and a part of other sensory systems in how a person functions. Additionally, there are other important systems that we are going to discuss in this book. The **somatosensory system** refers to the integration of the visual and proprioceptive systems in order to perceive and respond with temporal and spatial organization, develop body scheme and postural response, stabilize the head and body during movement, and interpret touch sensation and pain needed for movements and actions.

Finally, **praxis**, or **kinesthesis** help us understand how to move our bodies. The praxic system, or the kinesthetic system essentially "puts it all together" when it comes to motor responses to sensory information that has been perceived by the other senses.

Putting it all together

Let's look at all of the sensory systems in a list:

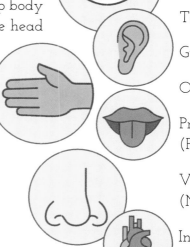

Visual System (Sight)

Auditory System (Sound)

Tactile System (Touch)

Gustatory System (Taste)

Olfactory System (Smell)

Proprioceptive System
(Position in space)

Vestibular System
(Movement)

Interoceptive System
(Inner body)

And the systems that are deeply connected to these sensory systems:

* Somatosensory System
(Movement organization)

* Praxic/Kinesthetic System
(How to move)

We'll go into further detail about each of the sensory systems and their relationship to a child functioning with sensory processing issues later in this chapter.

Even with the large list of sensory systems outlined above, there are three areas that are primary influencers on the integration of our senses.

The proprioceptive, vestibular, and touch senses are primary influences on the integration of our senses. The three senses are not only interconnected but are also connected with other systems in the brain. This happens from infancy as we are swaddled, carried in a flexed position, and swung in a baby swing or our mother's arms. If these sensory systems are poorly functioning, a child will have trouble developing in all areas. Integration of the vestibular and proprioceptive systems gives the child control over eye movements at infancy. Without integration of these two systems, the baby will be slow to develop postural reactions and have a poor foundation of movement.

If the proprioceptive, vestibular, and touch sensory systems are not functioning adequately, an individual will have a poor reaction to his environment. He may withdraw or over-respond to auditory and visual stimuli. The child cannot focus on tasks and may feel insecure in his environment. These problems can lead to a poor body perception.

Typically, dysfunction within these three systems present in many different ways. A child with sensory difficulties may be over- or under-responsive to sensory input. They may operate on an unusually high or unusually low level of activity. They may fatigue easily during activity or may constantly be in motion. Children may fluctuate between responsiveness, activity levels, and energy levels.

Additionally, children with sensory processing dysfunctions typically present with other delays. Development of motor coordination, fine motor skills, gross motor skills, social-emotional skills, behaviors, executive functioning skills, language, and learning are all at risk as a result of impaired sensory processing.

It is important to note that sensory processing is deeply connected to a combination of the sensory systems working together as well as the impact of environmental stimuli. Sensation from the environment is combined with family life, parent expectations, peer interactions, classroom rules, community expectations, internal states such as feelings, hunger, fatigue, and health to result in behaviors responses. Looking at the underlying reasons for behavioral responses is absolutely key to identifying strategies to help with behaviors. This refers to the "big picture" discussed in Chapter 1 and is the root to determining an effective sensory diet.

The Big Three Sensory Systems

There are three sensory systems that have a primary influence in sensory-related responses. The sensory systems described below include all of the systems of the body despite the primary influences of the proprioceptive, vestibular, and tactile systems. In general, the child who experiences a need for a sensory diet has differences in sensory responsiveness from one or more of the systems that results in poor modulation, perception, or discrimination of sensory information.

The **Tactile Sensory System** is one of the earliest developed senses of the body. The skin is the largest and the most prevalent organ. The skin performs unique duties for the body. Most importantly, the skin protects and alerts us to danger and discriminates sensation with regard to location and identification. These two levels of sensation work together yet are distinctively important. Discrimination of touch allows us to sense where a sensation is felt on the body. With discrimination, we are able to discern a fly that lands on our arm. The second level of the tactile system alerts us to danger. It allows us to jump in response to the "fight or flight" response when we perceive a spider crawling on our arm. The information received from the tactile system also includes light touch, pain, temperature, and pressure.

When either of these levels of sensation are disrupted, tactile dysfunction can result. This presents in many ways, including hypersensitivity to tags in clothing, a dislike of messy play, difficulty with fine motor tasks, a fear of being touched by someone without seeing that touch, a high tolerance of pain, or a need to touch everything and everyone.

When the tactile system is immature or impaired, the brain can become overly stimulated with resulting poor organization and regulation of input. Children can then experience difficulty with behavior and concentration as a result.

Treatment for the child with an impaired tactile

sensory system focuses on providing a variety of deep- and light-touch experiences (Koomar & Bundy, 1991). Additionally, resistance activities, much like those indicated for decreased discrimination of vestibular and proprioceptive information, may be used in the therapeutic sensory diet.

When it comes to the tactile sensation of foods, hyper-responsiveness to certain textures of foods or drinks can interfere with an individual's ability to tolerate certain foods or liquids. Trial desensitization strategies to food. A qualified occupational therapist should intervene with these strategies. Promote a positive attitude during mealtimes. Allow the individual to eat preferred foods and drinks at mealtimes while introducing new foods at different times during the day.

Hyper-responsiveness of the tactile sense may present in a child as over-responsiveness or overreaction to tactile sensation. This looks like:

- Overly sensitivity to temperature including air, food, water, or objects
- Withdrawing when touched
- Refusing certain food textures
- Dislike of having face or hair washed
- Dislikes of hair cuts
- Dislikes of having fingernails cut
- Excessively ticklish
- Avoidance to messy play or getting one's hands dirty
- Avoidance of finger painting, dirt, sand, bare feet on grass, etc.
- Clothing preferences and avoidances such as resisting shoes or socks

NEXT PAGE >

- Annoyance to clothing seams or clothing textures
- Resistance to hair brushing
- Overreactions to accidental or surprising light touches from others
- Avoids affectionate touch such as hugs

Adaptations/Accommodations address hyper-responsiveness to the tactile sense:

- Deep pressure activities using couch cushions or a bean bag
- Make a DIY crash pad using a duvet cover and stuffed animals/pillows
- Deep pressure with wall push-ups, standard push-ups, half push-ups, one-handed push-ups
- Joint compressions (Compressions must be completed accurately and consistently and instructed by an occupational therapist)
- Brushing technique (This must be completed accurately and consistently and instructed by an occupational therapist)
- Body socks
- Bear hugs
- Therapy ball to roll on the child's back as they lie supine (on the back) or prone (on the belly)
- Sit on therapy ball and bounce
- Therapy band exercise
- Log roll
- Resistive play dough
- Back scratch/firm back rub
- Weighted vest

- Weighted lap pad
- Weighted blanket
- Weights on the knees when sitting at a desk
- Ankle weights for a walking break
- Wrist weights for arm motions
- Water play with a scrub brush
- Roll up in a blanket "burrito"
- Warm bath
- Calming sensory input during and after a tactile sensory activity

Hypo-responsiveness of the tactile sense may present in a child as under-responsiveness or underreaction to tactile sensation. This may look like:

- Seeks out tactile sensory input
- Bumps into others
- High pain tolerance
- Stuffs food in mouth
- Licks items or own skin
- Not aware of being touched
- Seems unaware of light touch
- Startles easily when touched
- When getting dressed, doesn't notice clothing that is twisted
- Tendency for self-abusiveness: biting self, rubbing self with heavy pressure, head-banging, pinching self, etc.
- Doesn't notice a runny nose, messy face, or messy hands
- Puts items in the mouth
- Lack of personal space
- Runs into other children without noticing
- Has difficulty maintaining space in line; bumps into others without noticing
- Falls out of chair
- NEEDS to touch everything
- Uses a tight pencil grip on the pencil
- Writes with heavy pencil pressure
- Tears paper when cutting with scissors
- Unintentionally rough on siblings, other children, or pets
- Always touching others or things
- Seeks out messy play experiences
- Prefers to rub or feel certain textures
- Difficulty with fine motor tasks
- Craves touch

Adaptations/Accommodations to address hypo-responsiveness to the tactile sense may include:

- Messy play activities
- Tactile materials and manipulatives in learning activities
- Fidget tools
- Keychain fidget tools
- Deep pressure activities
- Sensory dough materials: goop, play dough, shaving cream, or paper mache
- Opportunities to practice location-awareness games: "I Spy" or "Hot and Cold"
- Weighted vest, weighted blanket, or weighted lap pad
- Therapy band or a movement component attached to classroom desks
- Velcro attached to the underside of a desk to help with attention and focus
- Stickers stuck on the underside of a desk so that the student can pick at the sticker to help with attention and focus
- Compression clothing
- Weight bearing activities before activities that require focus and attention
- Visual schedule

Several areas of development may be delayed or affected in the child with an impaired tactile sensory system. These may include:

- Delayed fine motor skills
- Poor body scheme
- Difficulty with praxis
- Poor hand skill development

SENSORY DIET TIP: Quiet and enclosed spaces such as a tent, cardboard box, or small room with pillows are effective places for children to apply tactile sensation. In these small, enclosed spaces, other forms of sensation are diminished.

The **Proprioception Sensory System** is the recognition and response to the body's position in space with an internal feedback system using the position in space of the joints, tendons, and muscles. This sensory system allows the body to automatically react to changes in force and pressure given body movements and object manipulation. The body receives more feedback from active muscles rather than passive muscle use. Related to the proprioception system is praxis or motor planning. Individuals are able to plan and execute motor tasks given feedback from the proprioceptive system. Praxis allows us to utilize sensory input from the senses and to coordinate that information to move appropriately.

Treatment for the child with an impaired proprioceptive sensory system focuses on providing intense proprioceptive information and improving postural responses.

Hyper-responsiveness of the proprioception sense may present in a child as over-responsiveness or overreaction to proprioceptive sensation. This may include postural insecurity. This may look like:

- Uses too little pressure when writing or coloring
- Prefers soft or pureed foods
- Appears lethargic

- Bumps into people or objects
- Poor posture, slumps in their seat
- Poor handwriting
- Inability to sit upright when writing or completing desk work; Rests with head down on arms while working
- Poor awareness of position-in-space
- Frequent falling
- Clumsiness
- Poor balance
- Poor body awareness
- Poor attention
- Poor motor planning

Adaptations/Accommodations to address hyper-responsiveness of the proprioception sense include the organizing, heavy work input that is listed below.

Some individuals can be overresponsive to proprioceptive input. For those individuals, proprioceptive input can seem scary or harmful. They will avoid heavy work input. For these individuals, it's important to find alternative calming activities.

Hypo-responsiveness of the proprioceptive sense may present in a child as under-responsiveness or underreaction to proprioceptive sensation. This looks like:

- Uses excessive pressure when writing or coloring
- "Jumper and crasher"- seeks out sensory input

NEXT PAGE >

- Can't sleep without being hugged or held
- Bumps into people or objects
- Seems aggressive
- Grinds teeth
- Walks on toes
- Chews on pencils, shirt, sleeve, toys, etc.
- Prefers crunchy or chewy foods
- Cracks knuckles
- Breaks pencils or crayons when writing or coloring
- Pinches, bites, kicks, or headbutts others
- Difficulty with fine motor skills
- Poor handwriting
- Poor awareness of position-in-space
- Stomps their feet on the ground when walking
- Kicks their chair or their neighbors chair in the classroom
- Frequent falling
- Clumsiness
- Poor balance
- Constantly moving and fidgeting
- Poor attention

Activities that provide input through the joints and receptors in the muscles/joints have a calming effect on sensory needs. Activities can be exercise-based (therapy bands, animal walks, jumping jacks, etc.) or they can be functional in nature (removing wet laundry from the washing machine, helping in the garden, vacuuming, etc.) Activities can also be easily incorporated into environments and schedules such as utilizing a sports bottle with a straw or

adding proprioceptive input into writing tasks with a weighted pencil. Activities below can be incorporated into an individual's day to address needs of the proprioceptive sense.

Adaptations/Accommodations to address proprioception needs may include:

- Heavy work input through push and pull activities such as tug-of-war
- Pulling a full wagon
- Pushing a wheelbarrow
- Pushing heavy chairs on a carpeted floor
- Moving furniture
- picking up and carrying a full laundry basket
- Shoveling snow or dirt
- Wearing a heavy backpack
- Mopping floors
- Carrying a stack of books
- Wall push-ups
- Chair push-ups
- Wall sits ("sit" with the back against the wall as if on an imaginary chair)
- Roll up in a blanket
- Massage
- Weighted blanket
- Weighted lap pad
- Wrist or arm weights
- Fidget tools or stress balls
- Therapy band on chair legs
- Joint compressions
- Jump on a trampoline
- Hops, Kicks, Jumps, Skipping, Stomping
- Massage through shoulders
- Deep pressure with couch cushions to create a "sandwich"

NEXT PAGE >

- Animal walks (bear walks, crab walks, donkey kicks, duck walks, etc.)
- Chewy foods
- Crunchy foods
- Chewing tool

The **Vestibular Sensory System** is the sense of movement and balance, and uses the receptors in the inner ear and allows the body to orient to position in space. The vestibular system is closely related to eye movements and coordination. Vestibular sensory input is a powerful tool in helping children with sensory needs. Adding a few vestibular activities to the day allows for long-lasting effects. Every individual requires vestibular sensory input in natural development. In fact, as infants we are exposed to vestibular input that promotes a natural and healthy development and integration of all systems.

The sensory vestibular activities listed in this book are playful ways to promote performance and tolerance to movement activities. They are also challenges against gravity to help kids with difficulties in equilibrium, balance, self-regulation, and adjusting to typical sensory input. The vestibular system operates through receptors in the inner ear and in conjunction with position in space, input from the eyes, and feedback from muscle and joint receptors, is able to contribute to posture and appropriate response of the visual system to maintain a field of vision. This allows an individual to detect movement and changes in the position of the head and body. Dysfunction in the vestibular system may result in hypersensitivity to movements or hyposensitivity to movements.

The receptors of the vestibular sensory system are actually hair cells that are found in two structures in the inner ear:

Receptors on the otolith organs within the ear respond to linear movement, gravity, and head tilt.

Receptors on the semicircular canals within the ear respond to angular movement of the head and quick movement changes.

These receptors provide information to the central nervous system about the body's position in space and project information to several areas:

✳ Cerebellum- Information received in the cerebellum is used to control posture, eye, and head movements.
✳ Oculomotor nuclei- Information received here help to correct the eyes with head and body movements.
✳ Spinal cord- Information received here helps with muscle tone and postural adjustments.
✳ Thalamus and cortex- Information received here helps with perception of motion and spatial orientation and integrates somatosensory information.

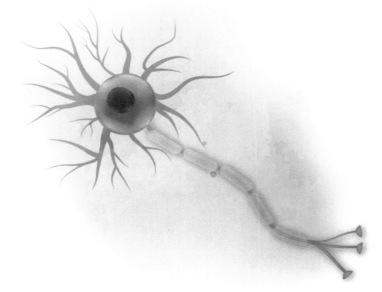

Problems with the Vestibular Processing System

There are many common features that may present in the child with vestibular sensory difficulties. These can be considered red flags, or warning signals of vestibular processing problems:

Poor visual processing
Poor spatial awareness
Poor balance
Difficulty with bilateral integration
Sequencing deficits
Poor visual-motor skills
Poor constructional abilities
Poor discrimination of body position
Poor discrimination of movement
Poor equilibrium
Subtle difficulties discerning the orientation of head
Trouble negotiating action sequences

When providing vestibular input as an intervention strategy for sensory needs, various movement patterns should be considered. Depending on the individualized needs of the child, activities can be designed to include movements such as:

Prone swinging
Seated swinging
Standing swinging
Linear movements
Vertical movements
Rotary movements
Angular movements
Upside down movements
Horizontal movements
Challenges to balance
Inverted head
Unstable base of support
Starts and stops in motion
Changes in direction
Changes in speed

Precautions for Vestibular Sensory Input

Vestibular input is extremely powerful. Negative reactions to sensations may not be apparent for several hours following input. Sensory overload or sensory disorientation can occur even when the child appeared to respond well to sensations during the actual activity or therapy session. Additionally, children with impaired sensory systems may not be able to recognize when they have reached a point of "too much" input during the treatment activity. Vestibular input can have lasting effects of up to 12 hours. Vestibular input should be provided in only short periods, especially when initiating a sensory strategy with a child. Sensory overload presents with pupil dilation, sweaty palms, changes in respiration, and disorientation.

When a child experiences difficulty with sensory discrimination and perception, there may be subsequent deficits in postural stability, visual-motor control, and motor planning. Functionally, these challenged areas result in diminished participation in childhood occupations such as play, school performance, or participation in family or community environments.

Treatment utilizing vestibular input should incorporate proprioceptive input and graded vestibular input, giving the child control of the amount and level of vestibular input. Treatment focuses on providing and improving postural responses in functional tasks.

Hyper-responsiveness of the vestibular sense may present in a child as over-responsiveness or overreaction to vestibular sensation. This may

look like:

- Experiences gravitational insecurity
- Overly dizzy with motions
- Resistant to moving activities such as swings, slides, elevators, or escalators
- Fear of unstable surfaces
- Unable to tolerate backward motions
- Unable to tolerate side to side motions
- Illness in moving vehicles
- Avoids swings or slides
- Gets motion sick easily
- Appears "clingy"
- Refuses to move from the ground (i.e. jumping or hopping activities)
- Difficulty/fear of balance activities
- Refusal to participate in gym class
- Fearful on bleachers or on risers
- Fear or dislike of riding in elevators or escalators
- Fearful of movement
- Dislike of spinning motions
- Avoids chasing games
- Overly fearful of heights
- Nauseous when watching spinning objects
- Poor posture
- Easily fatigued
- Poor coordination
- Low muscle tone
- Poor motor planning
- Fearful when a teacher approaches or pushes in the child's chair
- Clumsiness
- Poor attention

Adaptations/Accommodations to address hyper-responsiveness of the vestibular sense:

- Skipping
- Prone activates with arms supporting the upper body at the shoulders and elbows
- Slowly adding activities in the quadruped positioning
- Adding a support for jumping, hopping, balance activities
- Crawling
- Walking
- Sliding
- Rolling
- Being pulled on a blanket or sled (indoor works, too!)
- Throwing beanbags at a target
- Throwing/catching a ball
- Movement obstacle courses
- Wheelbarrow races
- Scooter activities in various positions (seated, prone)
- Throwing and catching bean bags
- Therapy ball in a variety of positions
- Yoga in modified positions

Hypo-responsiveness of the vestibular sense may present in a child as under-responsiveness or underreaction to vestibular sensation. This may look like:

- Constant movement including jumping, spinning, rocking, climbing
- Craves movement at fast intervals
- Craves spinning, rocking, or rotary motions
- Poor balance on uneven surfaces

- Constantly fidgeting
- Increased visual attention to spinning objects or overhead fans
- Bolts or runs away in community or group settings, or when outdoors or in large open areas such as shopping malls
- Difficulty maintaining sustained attention
- Impulsive movement
- Constantly getting up and down from desk in the classroom
- Walks around when not supposed to (in the classroom, during meals, etc.)
- Loves to be upside down
- Head banging
- Leans chair back when seated at a desk
- Loves spinning
- Rocks self-back and forth when seated
- Poor posture
- Poor coordination
- Poor motor planning
- A deep need to keep moving in order to function
- Frequent falling
- Clumsiness
- Poor balance
- Poor attention

Adaptations/Accommodations to address hypo-responsive of the vestibular input:

- Utilize a cushion when required to sit for periods of time in the classroom or during meals
- Heavy work before sustained attention

NEXT PAGE >

- Therapy band or motion incorporated into seating
- Alternative seating systems
- Therapy ball
- Fidget tools
- Cushion or partially deflated beach ball on the floor under feet at a desk or chair.
- Tie therapy band (TheraBand) or a resistive cord around the legs of a student's chair for use as a foot fidget
- Provide appropriate play-based opportunities for movement needs (sit and spin toy, see saw toy, rocking chair, trampoline)
- Weave vestibular input throughout the day and prior to fine motor/visual motor activities
- Ensure the feet touch the ground or have support when seated in a chair or on the toilet

The remaining sensory systems

Because the sensory system is so closely interacting, each of the systems work together and in a coordinated manner. The main three sensory systems (tactile, proprioception, and vestibular) are power houses when it comes to energy level in kids. But the other sensory systems can have calming or alerting effects as well. Let's talk about each system and how sensory strategies associated with each system can be a beneficial part of a sensory diet.

The Visual System

Eighty percent of the information we receive from our environment is visual. When perception of this information is not processed correctly, it can create an altered state that influences many areas: eye-hand coordination, postural reflexes, and vestibular processing are all influenced and reliant upon the visual system. The visual system is the sensory system that most individuals rely upon most heavily for daily tasks. Visual information is perceived by cells in the back of the eye. These cells (rods and cones) relay and transfer light information into information that is transferred to the central nervous system. These photoreceptors are able to perceive day time vision and night time vision, with adjustments to sensitivity of light intensity. They are able to respond to different spectrum of color and differentiate color information. The rod and cone cells, along with the retina, process a great deal of visual information in the neural structure of the eye before transmitting information to the central nervous system.

The relay of information from the eyes to the central nervous system are made up of three pathways.

Pathways project to different areas of the brain and allow for

a) processing and recognition of faces/shapes/motion (the "what" and "where" of objects),

b) integration of information in order to coordinate posture and eye movements, and

c) oculomotor adaptation.

Hyper-responsiveness of the visual sense may present in a child as over-responsiveness or overreaction to visual sensation. This may look like:

- Complains of lights being too bright
- Unable to tolerate certain lighting such as fluorescent overhead lights
- Struggles with sudden changes in lighting
- Challenged by bright or flashing lights
- Colorful lights "hurt" the eyes
- Complains of headaches in bright light
- Complains of the "glow" of unnatural lighting
- Distressed by light sources
- Sensitive to light
- Sensitive to certain colors
- Distracted by cluttered spaces
- Avoids eye contact

Adaptations/Accommodations to address hyper-responsiveness of the visual sense:

- Dim light in a variety of environments
- Natural lighting
- Hat with a visor to reduce overhead lighting
- Sunglasses or shaded lenses
- Use social stories
- Use calming or low lights
- Remove objects hanging from the ceiling
- Use muted colors
- Use visual supports and organizers

Hypo-responsiveness of the visual sense may present in a child as under-responsiveness or underreaction to visual sensation. This looks like:

- Attracted to spinning objects
- Difficulty with visual perception
- Difficulty with eye-hand coordination
- Difficulty with reading and writing
- Holds or presses hands on eyelids in order to see flashing lights
- Squints or presses eyelids shut
- Flaps hands or objects in front of eyes

Adaptations/Accommodations to address hypo-responsiveness of the visual sense:

- Added time for student to incorporate needed sensory input into the day
- Visual tools such as visual puzzles, "I Spy" pages, mazes, word searches
- Sunglasses or shaded lenses
- Physical prompts to point out important visual information
- Variety of colored pencils/pens in handwriting
- Physical guide tool to maintain the place on a page when reading or writing

Oculomotor Motor Function

Oculomotor function refers to the six muscles surrounding each eye. These muscles work together to produce controlled eye movements. When there is dysfunction of oculomotor function, a child may have difficulty with depth perception, visual attention, visual memory, visual perceptual tasks, visual scanning, spatial disorientation, eye-hand coordination, balance, or reading and writing tasks. You can see how these difficulties closely resemble problems that result from vestibular or proprioceptive dysfunctions. If oculomotor dysfunction is suspected, an eye exam should be performed.

Therapeutic interventions for oculomotor dysfunction

NOTE: Indicators for difficulty in oculomotor function should not be used as a diagnostic tool or used to label a deficit as oculomotor dysfunction. The activities below should be used as appropriate by an occupational therapist trained in visual therapy or behavioral optometrist.

Try these activities if oculomotor dysfunction is a definitive diagnosis:

* Balance boards can be used in a variety of games and activities.

* Directional jumping can be completed using visual directions such as words or arrows.

* Hopscotch is a great way to incorporate visual-motor skills and learning when incorporating components such as sight words, colors, numbers, etc.

* A balance beam can be used indoors or outdoors and in myriad ways.

* Use a Brock String to address convergence insufficiency, convergence, suppression of the eye, and other oculomotor dysfunctions.

* Visual tracking tools and activities can be used in play.

* Utilize crawling activities. Crawling through an obstacle course with a bean bag or pillow on the child's back is one strategy. The child can crawl along a masking tape course while keeping the object from falling from their back.

* Hit a soft ball/balloon/crumbled paper with a tennis racket or paddle.

* Play with a zoom ball used while the child attempts to watch the ball with their eyes as it moves toward and away from them.

* Toss a large beach ball with letters or words written on it. When the child catches the ball, they should look at and say one word that is closest to their hands.

* Toss bean bags and watch as the bean bag sails into its target.

* Create a marble run and watch as the marble glides through the toy.

The Auditory System

Receptors for the auditory system are located in the inner ear and are responsible for receiving vibration from sound waves and changing them to fluid movement energy. Information is projected to the central nervous system and transmits sound frequency as well as timing and intensity of sound input. The auditory system is integrated with somatosensory input in order to play a role in controlling orientation of the eyes, head, and body to sound.

Treatment activities may provide alerting input that help the child become more aware of their sensory needs through their mouth. They are activities that calm and add focus so that children can better attend to their environment and sensory input or needs is less of a primary focus.

Hyper-responsiveness of the auditory sense may present in a child as over-responsiveness or overreaction to auditory sensation. This may look like:

> - Startles easily to unexpected sounds
> - Dislikes noisy places
> - Overly sensitive to speakers on radios
> - Fearful of smoke detectors, overhead speakers
> - Shushes others or asks others to stop talking
> - Holds hands over ears
> - Sensitive to certain sounds such as lawnmowers or the hum of the refrigerator
> - Easily distracted by sounds and background noise
> - Hums to block out background noise

Adaptations/Accommodations to address hyper-responsiveness of the auditory sense:

> - Calming auditory input: fill a plastic bottle with rice to use as a sensory sound tool
> - Use foam earplugs
> - Use earbuds or headphones to dull sounds, especially in noisy environments
> - Soft/calm music
> - Add soft material like felt or cut tennis balls to the bottoms of desk chairs and desks

> - Allow student to travel hallways minutes before other students to reduce noise

Hypo-responsiveness of the auditory sense may present in a child as under-responsiveness or underreaction to auditory sensation. This looks like:

> - Seems to be unaware of sounds
> - Holds radio speakers up against ears
> - Doesn't respond to alarms
> - Makes silly sounds at inappropriate times or frequently
> - Mimics sounds of others
> - Talks to self
> - Difficulty locating sounds, especially when in a noisy environment
> - Hums in order to hear the sound of humming

Adaptations/Accommodations to address hypo-responsiveness of the auditory sense:

> - Utilize visual schedules or visual prompts
> - Utilize a physical prompt or "secret code" to indicate a transition
> - Slow down speech when giving directions
> - Seat child away from hallways, windows, or busy areas
> - Trial a whisper phone in the classroom
> - Teach child to tap out instructions or repeat instructions

The Gustatory System

The gustatory system perceives input through the tongue. Taste cells in the mouth perceive five sensations: salty, sweet, bitter, sour, and savory. The gustatory system is closely related to the sense of smell and proprioception. How we perceive taste is deeply influenced by the sense of smell.

While many children with sensory needs have a tendency to chew on their shirt collars or pencils as a sensory strategy in order to seek proprioception needs, the behavior may occur as a result or as a reaction to under-responding to oral input.

Other children may seek out intense taste sensations and in that case put non-edible items into their mouth to satisfy that sensory need. Still other children may over-respond or under-respond to certain flavors or taste sensations. For those children, it is common to experience food refusal related to texture or taste.

Activities provide proprioceptive input that help the child become more aware of their sensory needs through their mouth. They are activities that enable the child to better attend to their environment so that the sensory component is less of a primary focus.

SENSORY DIET TIP: Mild tastes may be overly perceived by some children. Help your child with to broaden the tastes he tolerates or likes, and use strong tastes he enjoys to help arouse his sluggish system.

Hypersensitivity to oral sensory input may present in a child as over-responsiveness or overreaction to gustatory sensation. This looks like:

- Dislike of mixed textures (cereal in milk or chunky soup)
- Resistant to trying new foods
- Avoids certain textures
- Avoids straws
- Avoidance of specific food or drink temperatures
- Picky eating
- Preference for bland foods
- Avoids temperature extremes (unable to tolerate hot or cold foods)
- Prefers foods that do not touch or mix on their plate
- Use of only a specific spoon or fork or no utensil at all
- Intolerance to teeth brushing.
- Anxiety or gagging when presented with new foods
- Drooling

Adaptations/Accommodations to address hyper-responsiveness of the gustatory sense:

> • Eat chewy snacks like fruit leather, raisins, dried fruit, licorice
> • Suck apple sauce through a straw
> • Drink smoothies with a straw
> • Use a sports cup with a long straw or a squeeze bottle that requires sucking
> • Blow bubbles
> • Blow a kazoo
> • Blow a harmonica
> • Blow a whistle
>
> • Blow up balloons
> • Use straws to suck, bite, blow cotton balls, small crackers, etc.
> • Chew toys or jewelry
> • Chew tools on pencil tops or Thera-tubing attached to a pencil top

Hypo-responsiveness of the gustatory sense may present in a child as under-responsiveness or underreaction to gustatory sensation. This may look like:

> • Licking objects
> • Bites others
> • Chews on clothing
> • Hums all the time
> • Prefers a vibrating toothbrush
> • Prefers spicy foods
> • Stuffs food into cheeks
> • Prefers food very hot or very cold temperature

Adaptations/Accommodations to address hypo-responsiveness of the gustatory sense:

> • Crunchy snacks like granola, dry cereal, trail mix, raw vegetables, brittle, pretzels, crackers, apples
> • Cold foods or drinks
> • Cold foods or drinks alternated or mixed with warm drinks like warm cider mixed with ice cubes or soup with a few ice cubes
> • Sour snacks or lemonade
> • Vibrating toothbrush

The Olfactory System

The olfactory system, or the system that enables the sense of smell, has receptors in the tissue of the nose that are connected by pathways to the brain. Connections occur via two pathways, one being a direct route to neurons in the brains and the second being a path that passes near the roof of the mouth. This channel is connected to the taste of foods.

There is some evidence indicating that the sense of smell is more associated with memory than the sense of vision or the other senses. The connection of the olfactory sense to the emotional part of the brain and previous experiences, as well as hypersensitivity or hyposensitivity to smells can cause anxiety or sensory related breakdowns in children with sensory processing difficulties.

There are many different ways to approach therapeutic intervention related to the olfactory sense.

✳ Different scents can be used in therapeutic manners. The child who is hypersensitive to scents can use unscented soaps and lotions.

✳ Try calming scents to soothe or relax: vanilla, floral, chamomile

✳ Try alerting scents to stimulate or alert: citrus, peppermint

✳ Use caution with essential oils and scents in general with children. Not all scents are safe for kids.

Hyper-responsiveness of the olfactory sense may present in a child as over-responsiveness or overreaction to olfactory sensation. This may look like:

- Overly sensitive to smells
- Notices smells others don't
- Anxious around certain smells
- Holds nose in response to certain scents

Adaptations/Accommodations to address hyper-responsiveness of the olfactory sense:

- Provide the child with tools scented with preferred scents (Wooden pencils can have a scent that interferes with a child's attention. A plastic mechanical pencil may be a better option.)
- Trial various laundry detergents/soaps to find a preferred scent (Unscented detergent can still produce a noxious scent for some individuals.)

Hypo-responsiveness of the olfactory sense may present in a child as under-responsiveness or underreaction to olfactory sensation. This may look like:

> • Smells unusual items like paper or certain materials
> • Prefers strong scents
> Adaptations/Accommodations to address hypo-responsiveness to the olfactory sense:
> • Preferred tools for use in the classroom and home
> • Preferred laundry detergents/soaps

The Interceptive System

The interoceptive sensory system is an area that most people are not as familiar with. This system is connected to amygdala, the emotional system, the limbic system, our emotional awareness, our feelings, and subconscious arousal. Receptors for the interoceptive system are in our organs and skin. The receptors relay information regarding feelings such as hunger, thirst, heart rate, and digestion to the brain. This is the foundation to sensations such as mood, emotions, aggression, excitement, and fear and in turn, promotes the physical response of our bodies.

Physical responses include functions such as hunger, thirst, feelings, digestion, heart rate, and body temperature.

In childhood development, it is important for a child to understand and label these inner sensations. When this acknowledgment occurs, it becomes natural to overcome them through problem solving ("If I'm hungry, I should eat") to develop self-awareness. When the system that registers this information is impaired, it can become quite confusing to the child.

There is a developmental curve to the interoceptive sensory system. Toddlers need a lot more external cues about what they are perceiving and how to identify the emotions or sensations they are experiencing. The children with sensation challenges are even more behind on this developmental level. They cannot figure out these internal clues. The connection of internal information to emotions or feelings AND environmental or social cues is very abstract for the child with sensory processing challenges.

Hyper-responsiveness of the interoceptive sense may present in a child as over-responsiveness or overreaction to interoceptive sensation. This may look like:

> • High pain tolerance
> • Distracted and overwhelmed by feelings of stress
> • Distracted or overly sensitive to sensations of stomach digestion
> • Distracted or overly sensitive to sensation of heart beat
> • Always hungry or thirsty
> • Eat more and more often to avoid feelings of hunger
> • Unable to sense the feeling of being full; overeats or overdrinks
> • Overwhelmed by feelings of sadness, anger, happiness, etc. and unable to respond appropriately
> • High urine output
> • Use the bathroom more often than

NEXT PAGE >

necessary to avoid feelings of a full bladder or bowel
- Distracted by changes in body temperature
- Distracted and overly sensitive to sweating
- Overly sensitive to feeling ticklish or itchy
- Overly sensitive to cold or heat
- Overly sensitive to signs of illness
- Fearful of vomiting

- Doesn't know when to go to the bathroom
- Never says they are hungry or thirsty
- Does not drink or eat enough
- Difficult to toilet train
- Never complains of being cold or hot (always wears shorts in the winter or pants in the summer)
- Never complains of sickness
- Difficulty falling asleep
- Unable to identify feelings of stress
- Unable to identify specific feelings and appropriate responses

Adaptations/accommodations to address hyper-responsiveness of the interoceptive sense:

- Calming vestibular activities such as slow and rhythmical bouncing or rocking
- Mindfulness activities
- Meditation
- Yoga
- Prone rolling over a therapy ball
- Proprioceptive input and "heavy work"
- Social stories to teach the child about sensations they experience and what that sensation means
- Timer for meals, drinks, bathroom

Hypo-responsiveness of the interoceptive sense may present in a child as under-responsiveness or underreaction to interoceptive sensation. This may look like:

- Low pain tolerance
- Poor or low response to interoceptive stimuli

Adaptations/accommodations to address hypo-responsiveness to the interoceptive sense:

- Alerting vestibular input prior to eating
- Utilize a visual schedule for toileting
- Timed schedule for bathroom
- Timed schedule for eating
- Timed schedule for drinking
- Alerting vestibular input prior to bathroom
- Inverted movements on therapy ball or therapy bolster
- Rotary movements on Sit and Spin toy, therapy scooter, swing
- Calming sleep techniques: weighted blanket, weighted stuffed animals, calming scents, warm bath, calming music, low music, back rub, joint compressions, lotion and massage, etc.
- Social stories
- Mindfulness activities
- Meditation
- Yoga

Chapter 3
The Who and What of a Sensory Diet

Sensory diet: the fix

Studies support the use of active participation in multi-sensory activities for at least 90 minutes per week to improve occupational performance and autism symptoms and behaviors (Fazlioglu & Baran, 2008; Thompson, 2011; Woo & Leon, 2013; Wuang, Wang, Huang, & Su 2010). Children who have a toolbox of sensory activities available to them for daily use may benefit from prescribed sensory activities. A sensory-based strategy guide can help.

Sensory diets are a commonly known strategy for addressing sensory needs. The term "sensory diet" was coined by Patricia Wilbarger in 1984 to explain how certain sensory experiences can improve occupational performance and help to remediate disruption of the sensory processing systems. A sensory diet is a means to adjust sensory input in relation to an individual's needs. A sensory diet is a meaningful set of strategies for developing sensory programs that are practical, carefully scheduled, and controlled in order to affect functioning. Sensory diet activities provide appropriate sensory input based on the needs of an individual. Just as a healthy diet consists of a variety of foods, a sensory diet is a balanced set of sensory information that allows an individual to function. A person cannot survive on broccoli alone. Similarly, a child cannot function with only one type of sensory activities.

Sensory diets are not just for kids with identified sensory issues. We all need a diet of sensory input. Most people naturally participate in conscious or subconscious acts that meet their specific needs. Consider the student who taps their pen against the desk while struggling on an exam. Consider the mother who paces while on the phone with her child's pediatrician. Consider the teenager who jiggles her leg while watching a movie. Consider the big yawn and stretch a person performs when climbing out of bed in the morning. Our bodies and minds instinctively know that varying sensory input allows us to function appropriately. Neurotypical children naturally seek out a variety of proprioceptive, vestibular, and tactile sensory input. As a result, they are able to accept and regulate other sensory input such as a seam in their shirt, a lawnmower running outside their classroom, or the scent of chicken cooking in the kitchen. Some individuals lack the ability or support to perform these sensory strategies without interventions.

What is a sensory diet?

A sensory diet is a set of activities that make up a sensory strategy and are appropriate for an individual's needs. These are specific and individualized activities that are scheduled into a child's day and are used to assist with regulation of activity levels, attention, and adaptive responses. Sensory diet activities are prescribed based on the individual's specific sensory needs. Just as there are no two people that are alike, there are no two sensory diets that are alike.

Every sensory diet should meet the specific needs of an individual whether in activity, position, intensity, time, sensory system, or type. Additionally, a sensory diet can be modified throughout the day and based on variances in tasks and can change over time. Specific types of sensory input from the various sensory systems are introduced during various times of the day and used to assist the brain in regulating attention and an appropriate level of arousal. A sensory diet provides the sensory input that a person's body craves to address underlying needs and improving visible and corresponding behaviors.

Sensory diets are used for many reasons:

* They regulate emotions and help a person to adjust to differing levels of alertness.

* They help improve attention span.

* Sensory diets allow individuals to tolerate sensations.

* They allow individuals to tolerate difficult or stressful situations.

* Sensory diets reduce unwanted sensory seeking behaviors or sensory-avoiding behaviors

* A sensory diet can reduce stress during transitions.

* Sensory diets can promote improved social participation and interaction in meaningful ways.

* A sensory diet can help individuals improve self-esteem and self-confidence.

* A sensory diet allows a person to transition from a state of over-reactiveness or under-reactiveness to a functional state of being.

Children in our modern times do not receive the heavy work input that they once did. Lifestyles of today limit the heavy work input that was once common place. Riding a bike to the store, walking to school, playing outside from morning until night, carrying jugs of water, and milking a cow are unknown tasks for most of today's children. There are more families with two working parents limiting daily involvement of a variety of sensory experiences. After school schedules limit the family's free time to run, roll down hills, and climb trees. Schools are cutting recess and physical education time limiting the physical activities during the school day.

What does all of this say about our children's sensory lifestyle? Simply put, there are less opportunities to experience a variety of movement and resistance in our daily lives. Modern lifestyle trends aren't the only reasons for a need for more sensory input during our day. Everyday tasks can put a person over the sensory edge, too. A trip to the grocery store before a big holiday means crowded aisles, a hot and stuffy center, with lots of visual and auditory input. It's not long before the average shopper feels over-heated, on edge, and NEEDS to get out of there!

Similarly, the child in a classroom who has been sitting too long begins to lose focus, wiggle and drop things, distract others, and fade from the learning environment. Sensory diets should perhaps be considered a sensory lifestyle. We all need heavy work, deep pressure, varying sensory input in order to process and adapt to our environments.

So, knowing all of these environmental and socio-economic components, what happens to the child with an impaired sensory processing system? They may already be struggling to accept sensory input or may over-react or under-react to the smallest sensation.

A sensory diet needs to be specific with thoughtful regard to timing, frequency, intensity, and duration of sensory input.

A sensory diet is a specific list of activity ideas designed on the needs of a particular individual. The hyposensitive child is one that seeks out sensory stimulation. These kids may benefit from intervals of alerting activities throughout the day in order to keep the child on task and focused.

The child who is hypersensitive to sensory input in the environment may benefit from calming activities to allow the child to center themselves and function in daily tasks or transitions.

Then, take into consideration the fact that each of these children with specific sensory needs have sensory-based preferences and dislikes. The

sensory diet is developed on an individual basis for each child's specific needs, goals, and motivation. Some children will respond well to one particular type of activity while other children with the same sensory profile will respond with entirely different behaviors and neurological responses.

The goal of a sensory diet is to improve modulation of sensation within daily routines. A sensory diet supports social engagement, self-regulation, behavior organization, perceived competence, self-esteem, and self-confidence.

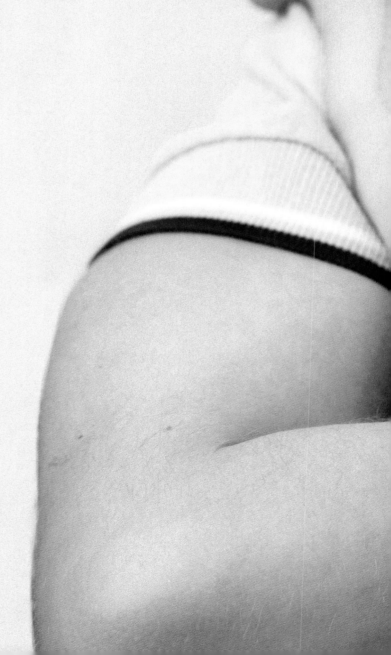

Additional intended goals of a sensory diet are to:

(1) Provide the child with predictable sensory information which helps organize the central nervous system

(2) Support social engagement, self-regulation, behavior organization, perceived competence, self-esteem, and self-confidence

(3) Inhibit and/or improve modulation of sensation within daily routines and environments

(4) Assist the child in processing a more organized response to sensory stimuli

Understand that challenging sensory-related behaviors often times occur when one is not prepared for them. Many times, a precursor to a meltdown may be disorganized periods of down time, a change in a schedule or routine. Every child will experience different precursors related to sensory responses. The goal of this book is to provide tactics for many situations and a toolbox of sensory diet strategies that can help prevent these periods of disorganization.

The ultimate goal is for the child to function, using skills independently, or by accommodations and modifications to their environment. As educators and systems of support to these children, it is easy to become caught up on the problem behavior and forgetting to target the precursor or underlying needs.

Sensory input is an acceptable strategy for many responses related to sensory needs. Sometimes undesirable behaviors impact an individual's ability to function or safely participate in a daily lifestyle. Some behaviors impact a family or classroom in a non-functional manner. These are behaviors that should be addressed in a manner that allows the individual to get the sensory input they need. Behaviors that can progress toward unhealthy or unfunctional manners may include:

Emotional overreaction
Meltdowns
Aggression
Hyper-attention
Difficulty with transitions
Inattention
Sleep issues
Impulsivity
Sensory-seeking behaviors
Sensory-resisting behaviors
Resistance to textures/food/clothing
Poor social Interactions

A note about meltdowns: Meltdowns (in a way that becomes unsafe or dysfunctional for the family or classroom on a consistent basis. Dysfunctional classroom or family life indicates a sensory need that is unmet. Meltdowns are a common result of those with sensory processing difficulties, those who may be unable to communicate needs, or those with emotional/social challenges. Consider meeting the need that creates the meltdown by analyzing needs and preferences.

Chapter 4
How to Create an Effective Sensory Diet

The Basics: How to Create a Sensory Diet

There are several levels of sensory diet creation. Each step requires intention and contemplation.

Clinical Strategizing of a Sensory Diet

A variety of research has shown that specific sensory applications can be effective in addressing sensory needs and in promoting function, and that the timing, intensity, and duration of sensory strategies are critical pieces of a sensory lifestyle (Wilbarger, 1995). Some research has also shown that specific sensory experiences play a part in influencing the structure, neurochemical makeup, and functional capabilities of the brain (Field, 1995).

As individuals, we tend to choose activities and experiences that are pleasurable. We enjoy snuggling up under a thick blanket at the end of the day. We tend to shy away from unpleasant sensations such as a static shock that happens every time we use that certain blanket. Likewise, some of us are thrill seekers and enjoy experiences like jumping from airplanes or bungee jumping. Others like to stay firmly on the ground and play it safe when it comes to leisure activities. Similarly, our clients or children who struggle with sensory processing can present with different preferences, as discussed in previous chapters of this book.

The key to successful integration of a sensory diet is ensuring the clinical strategizing and application are fit into the specific needs of the individual.

Application of a sensory diet involves several steps that can't be dismissed.

* Analyze/Identify
* Strategize
* Apply
* Monitor

IMPORTANT: Recognize that in the scope of this book, "behavior" indicates the way in which one acts or conducts oneself. Behaviors may not be intentional or deliberate, but a response of underlying sensory-based needs.

Level 1: Analyze/Identify- The first level in creation of a sensory diet requires identification of sensory related behaviors, attention issues related to impaired sensory input, challenges with focus or emotional regulation as a result of sensory needs, or meltdowns that impair functioning. This level of sensory diet creation requires assessment and identification of each challenging issue. Sensory behaviors should be identified and charted. This includes jotting down when specific behaviors occur, the setting where meltdowns occur, and antecedent to the behavior. Sensory related issues can be charted in a methodological manner or they can simply be written down on a scrap paper. The point is to identify the issues through analyzation.

> *Use the Sensory-Related Behavior Data Collection Form in the addendum section of this book.*

Level 2: Strategize/Reasoning- The next level in creating a sensory diet involves identifying the "why" behind the behaviors. Is it an unmet sensory need that causes a child to bolt down the hallway? Is the reason the child chews on all of their clothes because they need more proprioceptive input? After dysfunctional behaviors are identified, the reason behind the behaviors should be described.

The Sensory-Based Behavior Screening Form in the addendum of this book can be used to identify the underlying sensory needs leading to a behavior or action.

> *Use the Sensory Diet Strategy Guide to create a recommended sensory strategy for existing sensory challenges. Notes can be added as special instructions.*

Level 3: Apply/Trial Various Sensory Strategies- In this stage of sensory diet development, strategies need to be trialed for effectiveness within the lifestyle of the child and family. Sensory strategies need to be incorporated as indicated across a variety of settings, based on various sensory needs as they change throughout the day. Each strategy should be assessed for effectiveness. A simple checklist can be completed in the classroom or at home. When a sensory strategy is determined to work, that activity can be added to the child's sensory diet.

If a particular sensory activity is determined to be ineffective, return to level one. As adults who work with or raise children we know the fluidity of childhood. Needs, strengths, interests, environment, and other areas can change as a child develops and grows.

> *Use the Sensory Diet Schedule in the Addendum of this book to create a checklist for sensory diet activities.*

Level 4: Monitor- At this stage in development of a sensory diet, strategies should be monitored for effectiveness. Strategies should be monitored on a frequent basis with regard to effectiveness. A subjective assessment can be completed by adults who oversee the child's sensory diet strategies.

Additionally, carryover of sensory strategies must be monitored. A list of prescribed activities that are not completed because they require exhaustive effort are not an effective strategy within the life of a family. Carryover of sensory strategies is extremely important in the home and in the classroom. If activities are not able to be carried out, then a different sensory strategy should be incorporated into the child's sensory diet.

Monitor sensory strategies on a daily basis using the Daily Sensory Diet Sheet and the Sensory Diet Schedule, found in the Addendum of this book.

Use the Sensory Diet Effectiveness Tool, found in the Addendum of this book, to monitor sensory diet results and strategies. This form should be completed after a sensory diet has been in effect for two weeks.

Setting up a Sensory Station

The success of integrating sensory activities into a functional sensory lifestyle depends on the initiation of a specific and individualized sensory diet program. There are organizing and preliminary concerns to consider when setting up a sensory station in the home, classroom, or clinic. Therapists can recommend specific and individualized strategies for maximizing sensory responsiveness. These strategies will ensure carryover, ease of integration into daily tasks, and success of sensory recommendations. A sensory diet station can result in a nurturing and effective sensory lifestyle. As stated previously, an effective sensory space is one that is enclosed and small. Given a safe space, children can more effectively tolerate sensory diet activities.

- Reduce visual distractions.
- Reduce auditory distractions.
- Control the sensory station environment with a place for every item.
- Other children may benefit from open containers with minimal items for sensory choices.
- Store sensory items bins or containers with lids. This allows for stacking and additional gross motor and fine motor proprioceptive input when storing, moving, opening, and closing containers.
- Introduce new sensory strategies in a floor play activity in the third person with preferred "characters" receiving and responding to sensory input.
- Use preferred schedule strategies for sensory diet activities: picture schedule cards, printed lists, or choices that require movement to move activities to specific bins.
- Furnish the sensory station with comfortable and soft furniture (bean bag chair, body pillow, fabric hung on walls, weighted pillows or large stuffed animals are some ideas) and soft surfaces such as a fuzzy rug. Movement choices such as a rocking chair can be covered with soft, calming surfaces like a throw or heavy blanket.
- Facilitate activity choices in child-centered choice selection. Use the choice selection strategies listed below. An organized process for activity selection allows the child to remain calm and focused during the sensory diet time.

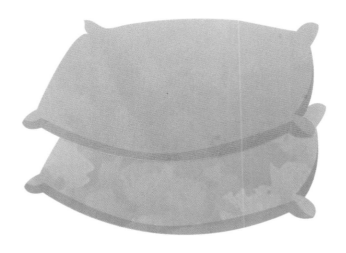

Sensory Diet Activity Selection Strategies

Once sensory diet strategies are developed, it's important to present them to the child in a clear manner. This will ensure carryover and success.

There are many ways to set up a sensory diet's scheduled activities. Each child may prefer an entirely different strategy for organizing sensory activities in their individualized sensory diet. The child who responds well to visual schedules in their classroom may use a picture schedule for their sensory diet. Scheduling sensory diet activities is important for carryover and use of appropriate sensory activities throughout the day and not after sensory overload or sensory seeking behaviors has occurred.

1. Picture Schedule - Take photos of sensory

activities. Print them out and laminate them. The photos can be added to a pocket in the front of each sensory bin or container. When the child takes out that activity, they can place the photo in a bowl or stick it to a wall planner using Velcro.

2. Clip Schedule - Use clothes pins to clip onto a schedule list of activities. When the child chooses a specific sensory activity, they can clip next to the words on their list.

3. Use PECS (Picture Exchange Communication System) or other pictures of sensory activities to create a keychain flip booklet of sensory diet activities.

4. Create strips of paper with sensory diet activities. Laminate the strips for sturdiness. Attach a self-sticking Velcro tab to the back of the laminated strip. The schedule of activities can then be attached to a felt board or schedule board with Velcro tabs. Once the activity is performed, the child can drop the strips into a cup. For a more durable system, use foam craft sticks or wooden craft sticks.

5. Create a sensory diet binder using page protectors. Children can mark off activities with a dry erase marker.

6. Visual Supports - Dry erase boards, Velcro board, flip picture schedule, felt boards are all ideas. Use visual supports in the simplest way possible with reduced visual distractions. A single color is best. Meeting the needs of the child is essential as well.

7. "First, Then" Strategy - Children with sensory processing challenges, particularly those on the Autism spectrum struggle with excessive instructions. It is hard for them to pull out the important words from a paragraph of instructions. Simplifying directions is key for these children. The "First, Then" strategy breaks down tasks into the simplest form. This is an effective mechanism for challenging behaviors and transitions.

8. Keychain schedule - Create a schedule that can go with the child. These can be clipped to belt loops, jackets, binders, necklaces, or backpacks. The options are limitless with a keychain schedule system. Use whatever strategy works best with the child. Some ideas are picture schedules, First/Then strategy, or even a dry erase schedule with words. A reward at the end of the schedule is a great reinforcer for children.

9. Special Interest Schedulers - Using the interests of the child as a motivator and as a scheduler can have great results. For the child who is interested in vehicles, they can attach a "wheel" onto a picture of a monster truck when each task is completed. The sky is the limit when it comes to using special interests in the form of schedules.

10. Apps and Technology - For some children, the use of a screen is the motivating tool that can help kids transition through their day. Special interests can be used in this manner as well. There are apps that utilize a form of the "First/Then" strategy combined with special interests such as characters like Sponge Bob.

11. Communication Center - Sensory diet activities can be created with visual images or words and made into magnets that are stuck to the refrigerator. Other ideas for a sensory diet center include a dry erase board or laminated paper that is used at a student's desk in the classroom or on the dining room table at home.

Guiding Success with Sensory Strategies

Once a child with sensory needs is set up with appropriate strategies for success, the sensory processing puzzle may STILL be incomplete. So many times, there are barriers to success with sensory strategies. These might be resistance from the child to try new things, difficulties with transitions, learned behaviors, resistance to stray from preferred activities, or a difficulty to incorporate necessary sensory activities into the child's lifestyle. Often times, the family life is so busy that it is difficult to make time for necessary

sensory input. Having choices is important for any child. For the child with sensory processing struggles, choices can be a big factor in compliance and carryover. Consider providing choices such as: which required activity to do first, when to receive reinforcers, how to do a required activity, the number of activities to do, and the order of required activities. Add these choices to the schedule system that works best with the individual child so their choice becomes "official" in the eyes of the child.

Structured days can be one strategy for success. It is very important to note, however, that the most effective sensory diet lifestyle is one in which sensory input is incorporated into natural activities. However, in order to maximize success, a structured guide may be the best technique for some children or the families. Consider the following options for adding more structure to a sensory lifestyle:

• Create a schedule of daily tasks (in as detailed or general as indicated by the child's needs).
• Make an open-ended activity more structured (Bus rides, lunch time, recess, free time).
• Utilize a specific sensory diet for difficult periods of time..

Monitoring Effectiveness of Sensory Input

It is essential that sensory diet components are monitored and assessed at regular intervals for effectiveness or contraindications such as over-responsiveness. Consider the aspects listed below when assessing for effectiveness of sensory diet activities. Watch, observe, and monitor the reactions and behaviors following sensory interventions.

Always consult an occupational therapist for appropriate interventions. Do not assume strategies in this book are recommendations for every child or every situation.

✱ Is there an adverse response?

✱ What is the change in reaction?

✱ Does the child experience a change in modulation?

✱ Does the child appear to exhibit a change in discrimination, regulation, postural control, praxis?

✱ What does outward behavior look like? Is the child's behavior organized?

✱ How is the child's self-esteem?

✱ How long do sensory activities take in order to see a difference in behavior or regulation?

Monitoring use of sensory diet strategies is an effective way to address any changes in sensory needs or modulation levels. Re-assessment should occur on a regular basis and when there are changes to the environment, health, or other contextual areas.

Carryover of Sensory Diet Recommendations

Once a sensory diet is established based on sensory needs and preferences, it is essential that the strategies are maintained. There are techniques that can be utilized to ensure the sensory diet is performed on a consistent and effective basis. Therapists are encouraged to find the "just right" level of activity, intensity, and duration for recommended interventions. Establishing a level of effectiveness ensures interventions are at a level between boredom and frustration. This approach is described as a "**just right challenge**" by Dr. Jean Ayres as a means for carryover of recommendations.

The Just Right Challenge allows for activities to fall within a balance between the challenge of the task and the skills of the person. When a challenge is too difficult, frustration will ensue. When the challenge is too low, boredom will result. An individual's abilities dictate how frustrating or easy a task is. As we know, every individual is vastly different, resulting in an array of just right levels that will be different for every individual. When that balance of difficulty and ease is established, a state of "flow", results in motivation. When intervention activities are designed in a way that a therapy client feels like they are utilizing all of their available skills, but are not so demanding that

the client finds the task too daunting, the Just Right Challenge is being utilized. Therapists will find that the Just Right Challenge is a powerful tool in initiating and sustaining engagement in occupation (Yerxa, 1990).

Carryover of therapy recommendations can be improved by various strategies: Modeling and teaching is one way that therapists can help with carryover. Explaining the "why" behind sensory diet activities as they relate to various sensory needs can help with parents and teachers utilizing the strategies. Modeling techniques that are to be used in the classroom or at home can be beneficial. Creating a sensory diet that is personalized and based on interests is an effective strategy for ensuring carryover. If the child has a deep interest in sensory activities based on preferences, the sensory diet activities become more fun as opposed to "work". Addressing feedback related to parent, teacher, and caregiver concerns related to sensory diet recommendations can have a big impact on carryover and use of sensory diet strategies. Ensure the members of a child's support system have a system for monitoring effectiveness of strategies and relaying feedback related to the sensory diet. Flexible strategies can be an essential tool for sensory diets. Allowing for activities to be fluid in incorporation can help with carryover. When a strict sensory diet is prescribed, including specific times and activities, the carryover will suffer. Families need to have methods for addressing fluctuations in schedules. Team goals are an important part of any therapy intervention. The overall goals of a child should be created in conjunction with parents, teachers, and the whole family. When the goals are jointly created, carryover will improve.

Chapter 5

Sensory Diet Tips

A sensory diet contains a specific list of activity ideas designed to meet the needs of a child. Before setting up the activities necessary for improved focus, attention, self-regulation, and sensory processing, it is important to recognize certain tips that can help with preparations and carry through of strategies. Consider these concepts as the pre-planning stage of developing a sensory lifestyle.

1. Parents should always consult an Occupational Therapist to lead them through activities that are appropriate for an individual child. A calming strategy may not be calming for every child and in every environment. Certain strategies can be downright dangerous to apply without appropriate training. Activities such as brushing, spinning, and deep pressure can have extreme adverse reactions when not applied correctly. It is beyond the scope of this book to address training in these areas. **Sensory strategies should NOT be considered "therapy at home" or a replacement for the intervention of an occupational therapist.**

2. The child should be assessed for participation in day to day occupations and over a range of challenges. Underlying precursors to behaviors should be identified. Is the child acting a certain way as a result of fatigue? Are they using compensatory strategies to get out of an undesirable activity as a learned response? Identifying what happened before the behaviors is key.

3. Communicate to others on the child's team. This may include the school principal, social worker, psychologist, teachers, paraprofessionals, bus attendants, therapists, pediatrician, relatives, and anyone who works with the child in some manner. Strategies should be added to the child's IEP. Education and communication of strategies that work well in each environment is necessary.

4. Sensory diet activities should be presented in a structured manner. Schedules and routines will ensure success of sensory diet strategies.

5. Activities in a sensory diet should always be supervised. Children should be strictly observed for non-verbal responses. Sensory diet activities are a valuable tool but precautions should be taken, particularly when setting

up a sensory diet or with younger children. For the child who is starting a new sensory diet, activities should be performed under direct supervision.

6. Anticipate sensory needs before there is need for sensory input. When behaviors are apparent, the child is beyond the point of addressing sensory needs. A behavioral response occurs after the body "crashes". For this reason, scheduled sensory diet input should be routinely provided, even if the child seems okay.

7. Observe the child, noting changes in sensory diet activities or levels of input. Children can become accustomed to routine sensory activities. With varying levels of environmental influence, there can be changes in sensory needs that can be accommodated for by slight variances in the sensory diet.

8. A predictable schedule is optimal for the child with sensory challenges. When there are changes in the daily schedule, outline them ahead of time when possible. In the home or classroom, this might look like a verbal and visual reminder. Sometimes schedule changes can cause distress. Refer to the section later in this chapter titled, Strategies to Help with Schedule Changes.

9. Set up a designated sensory diet area with limited visual and auditory distractions. Store sensory diet items

in containers that are specifically used for therapeutic intervention. When the sensory diet routine has become integrated, automatic, and independent, the child is then able to choose items during free play.

10. It's typically recommended to allow children to administer tactile or proprioception sensations to themselves. They then select the area, pressure, and length of time for stimulation themselves. It is preferable that sensory strategies are self-selected, self-initiated, and self-organized (Wilbarger, 1995).

11. Deep pressure is the most effective type of tactile sensation for decreasing tactile defensiveness, however some children prefer light touch or moving touch sensations (Ayres 1979).

12. Tactile sensations may be more tolerable when applied in the direction of hair growth and on arms, legs, and back.

13. Many times, children with sensory processing problems get "stuck" doing preferred activities as part of their sensory diet. These activities become a routine and are a structured course that they can anticipate. Add varied or novel sensory activities using a preferred theme or interest.

14. Use direct and simple statements in instruction when introducing sensory strategies. For many children with

sensory processing challenges, using simpler sentence structure can result in better comprehension and compliance.

15. Consider potential underlying behavioral motives for meltdowns. A behavior can become a mechanism for getting out of an undesirable task. Sometimes, children will want to get out of a task and use the meltdown strategy as a way to have that task removed. This type of behavior can occur in classroom settings or in the home when undesirable tasks must be completed. The child may want to get out of a particular activity and know that if they act out in such a way that it is distracting for other students, they will be removed from the classroom, or receive a sensory break. It may be that the child experienced reinforcement to a similar precursor or other preferred activity. This may not be intentional, it is just a strategy that has worked for them in the past. Likewise, this is not always the case. Children may really experience a sensory breakdown that has nothing to do with intentional behaviors. Analysis of precursors is essential for this reason.

16. Consider practicing sensory diet strategies outside of the natural environment. A one-on-one situation may be a better setting for introducing and addressing concerns. The goal is to use these strategies in the natural setting and with peers, but sometimes that extra practice can help some kids.

Use these strategies to encourage and maximize participation in the teaching of sensory diet strategies. These strategies can be utilized to ensure carryover of sensory input into a consistent sensory lifestyle.

* Utilize positive reinforcement. Positive reinforcement is the dessert to a sensory diet. It can include preferred play activities (adding in sensory rich ways to play).

* Consider a variety of reinforcement tactics. Try adding additional reinforcers by combining a new strategy to a preferred strategy.

* A timer is a helpful tool for the visual and auditory cue needed during activities.

* If-Then visual calendars can be helpful in encouraging participation.

* Video self-monitoring may be done in the home, clinic, or classroom. Record a child's participation in a sensory activity and play the video back as a teaching tool. Video recordings can also be made of another person completing the sensory task and used as a teaching mechanism. Some children respond well to seeing the way others respond to sensory input and activities.

* Simplify instructions when teaching.

* Role-play can help students visualize

how activities and sensory input work.

* Social Stories can be used to encourage participation.

* Use an app to provide reminders to take sensory breaks. A timer or scheduler app would work in this regard. App options include: Brain Works, Sensory Treat, Just Reminder, and To Do Reminder are some ideas.

* Identify possible antecedents to sensory-related behaviors. Consider what the child is getting out of the behavior.

Strategies to Help with Schedule Changes

It can be frustrating to devise a detailed plan to meet the needs of a child only to be derailed by the smallest inconsistency. Typically, children with sensory needs are overly sensitive to change. New activities or schedules can send a child into a sensory meltdown. There are strategies to help with schedule changes, or changes in a scheduled sensory activity. Not all of these techniques should be used with every child and not all at the same time. These are ideas that can be tried with the child to encourage effective responses.

> • Provide a consistent and calm response to sensory-related behaviors.
> • Offer assistance with the task.
> • Provide verbal, visual, or physical prompts to return the child to the

appropriate activity.
> • Create and use a child-friendly contract.
> • Utilize if-then terminology.
> • Use a picture schedules or checklists for activity or schedule changes.
> • Provide preferred activities as a task reward.

Sensory Diet Precautions

According to Merriam-Webster, a precaution refers to a measure taken beforehand to prevent harm or secure good. Precautions are a safeguard taken to prevent possible harm. In the case of sensory diets, precautions are used to prevent injury to the child. They are necessary to prevent overstimulation or injury. These sensory diet precautions should be understood before beginning any sensory activities as part of a sensory diet or intervention strategy.

> • Spinning and other vestibular activities are very strong sensory tools. A spinning activity should last no longer than 8-10 minutes and will yield results for up to 12 hours after the sensory activity has been completed. Spinning activities should always be supervised in the child with sensory processing concerns.
>
> • Later in this book, themed sensory diet strategies are discussed. When a themed

NEXT PAGE >

65

set of activities becomes common-place in a child's daily schedule, it can be beneficial to back off on the special interest sensory diet activities. When a child is able to participate, and tolerate a specific sensory activity using the special interest tool, it can be beneficial to remove the themed item from the activity on some occasions. This can reset the child's participation and over-exposure to the activity. It can also be a way to expose the child to sensory activities without the themed tool.

• Sensory diets should be trialed under strict observation. Some activities may seem to work sometimes but then not others. When that situation occurs, it is important to look at the environment, social interactions, transitions, and challenges that led up to the behavior. Sometimes, sensory interactions can result in a sensory breakdown in kids. Be sure to give activities second and even third chances to be sure sensory responses are typical.

• The sensations provided through sensory diets are adaptive supports. Sensations that are not providing optimal outcomes in functional tasks, then it is not an appropriate sensory choice for the child's sensory diet.

• Sometimes, a child responds adversely to new sensory input. A child who begins therapy services may suddenly behave with much more responsiveness throughout their day. When first starting therapy interventions, these adverse responses can be quite typical. It is important to remember that the child's ability to perceive situations and respond to sensory input has increased. The child, however, is not yet capable of dealing with the new and increased perception and resulting responses. The child will therefore require re-direction and channeling of attention until those behaviors lessen. Negative effects of sensation input may not appear immediately after an activity and may present after several hours. (Fisher & Bundy, 1989).

• Sensory diet strategies can require repetition and trial and error. Activities should be introduced deliberately and with intention. Activities should be monitored for effectiveness. It should be understood that activities can seem to "not work" at first. It takes time and purposeful strategizing to create an effective sensory diet.

• Other children may grow out of their special interest areas. The child who loves trains at age four may no longer express interest in Thomas the Train and other train themed activities when they are five years of age. Growing out of interest sets is common for kids of all ages. When this occurs, themed sensory diets can be adjusted to include the activities without the themed item or a different special interest sensory diet can be brainstormed.

• Some activities are specifically designed to alert a child that is having a difficult time staying aroused. It is essential to consult with an OT or COTA before using sensory diet activities to make sure that the child is truly under-aroused and not in a shut-down state.

Some signs of under stimulation are:

- Lethargy/Falling asleep
- Slumped posture
- Decreased attention
- Slow moving
- Decreased ability to follow directions
- Drooling or open mouth posture

Using the tips and precautions outlined in this chapter can be helpful in creating a successful sensory diet that results in better use of sensory strategies across all environments. The remaining chapters in this book outline specific sensory diet activities that can be incorporated into a child's day, leading to a sensory-friendly lifestyle and improved participation, attention, self-regulation, and sensory processing.

Signs of hyper-alertness are:

- Sweating
- Pallor
- Quick change from organized and focused behavior to disorganization

Sensory diets should be incorporated into the daily routine and not a performed as a disjointed task. Successful sensory diets are part of a sensory lifestyle!

As mentioned earlier in this book, the occupations of a child all need to fit together. Children need to engage in sensory strategies that allow them to participate in their life and the lifestyle of their family. Sensory diets are a means to engage them in occupations and situations. Sensory strategies should be used as a way to enrich the experiences of a task, adding sensory input when and how it is needed. In this manner, a sensory diet that spans multiple periods of the day as well as various environments has the potential to improve the whole family's quality of life.

Occupation-Specific Sensory Diet Strategies

A child's primary occupation is play. However, most children have other meaningful occupations as well: student, church-member, community member; The list could go on and on. It can be helpful for children to use occupation-specific sensory diet strategies in order to ensure carryover of a sensory lifestyle.

Sensory Diet Strategies for the School Day

The school day is a long period of the day in which high demands are placed on the individual with sensory or self-regulation challenges. Consider all of the demands placed on the child during a typical school day. Sensory diets in the school environment is a topic that could be its own book!

Students in the classroom are bombarded with directions, stimulation, and challenges and may struggle to process all of that input in a functional and effective manner. The child who presents with behaviors, poorly integrated sensory processing, attention, emotional regulation, self-regulation or any of the sensory-related responses indicated previously in this book can benefit from a sensory diet in the school environment. (Many children who do NOT present in one of these sensory-related situations can benefit from sensory breaks and sensory input, too!)

In these cases, a simple handout of sensory-related information can be a big help. As readers of this book, you have access to a printable packet on sensory processing. These packets can be printed off and used as educational information to those in the school environment. Get access to this printable booklet on The OT Toolbox website here: http://www.theottoolbox.com/2017/06/sensory-processing-disorder-information.html.

Adding sensory input within the school day is an

essential tactic for the child with sensory challenges and self-regulation needs. Incorporating sensory input within an educational platform can be done through modifications and adaptations to the classroom, as well as through kinesthetic learning. Some of these adjustments can be completed with the whole classroom, while others are techniques made based on individual needs.

> • Provide alternative seating, including bean bags, cushions, partially deflated beach balls, pool noodles added to the seat, therapy balls, etc.
> • Allow students to stand at elevated desks or at easels.
> • Encourage students to move and lift weighted bins within classroom tasks.
> • Provide heavy weighted tasks and jobs for students such as erasing chalkboards, clapping erasers, moving desks and chairs, and sliding classroom rugs to a different position within the classroom space.

School Sensory Diet

Provide opportunities for active resistance while seated in a desk chair: chair push-ups, chair/body squeezes, therapy band tied to the chair legs, hand gripper exercises, leaning on upper extremities, weighted vest, or lap pad.

Provide hand fidget activities: Fidget tool attached to the desk, Velcro applied to the inside or underside of a desk surface, hand "spider" push-ups, rubber band stretches, fidget balls, therapy putty, or pencil aerobics.

Trial seating options for linear motion, including inflatable cushions, T-stool, therapy ball, peanut ball, rocking chair, or a chair with one or two slightly shortened legs for rocking.

Use seating modifications including a solid seat with armrests of correct height, tilt-top desk, dycem to stabilize objects on desk, and a visual cue on the desk for paper placement.

Provide visual organization strategies such as simplified instructions, colored folders to organize subject matter, or a daily schedule.

Allow use of therapy band to encourage pulling tasks while stabilizing with one arm and moving with the other.

Provide brain break opportunities.

Provide a calm down space in the classroom with a bean bag, soft carpet, headphones, and sensory bin.

For the child with tactile defensiveness, provide deep pressure input, active resistance activities, finger fidgets, and resistive hand activities.

Encourage organizing input throughout the day via the use of active resistance or heavy work activities.

Allow the child to wear their backpack when travelling throughout the school.

When travelling throughout the school, require that the child holds onto someone when ascending

or descending stairs, and has a "safe" classroom environment with no items on the floor and no extraneous material (e.g., scatter rugs) if necessary.

Provide a separate desk space area with visual borders such as "walls" created by classroom furniture to reduce visual distractions during desk work.

Provide extra space to prevent incidental touch by others.

Designate spaces for circle time (e.g., carpet square or taped area of the floor).

Approach the child from the front and warn the child before touch.

Use firm touch and avoid light touch.

Minimize other possible overwhelming environmental stimuli by using natural lighting and curtains over the windows.

Shut the classroom door and blinds during periods of the day.

Use rubber bottoms on the chair and desk legs to reduce auditory impact.

Ensure a firm, supportive seat and that the desk and chair fit appropriately.

Play and break activities that provide resistance and heavy work input, "How Does Your Engine Run?" program (Williams & Shellenberger, 1994).

Provide extra space during games in the playground and gym class.

Provide visual or physical borders in the classroom or hallway (taped lines, wikki stick lines, pool noodles).

Provide a carpet square or felt square for students to sit on during circle time.

Reduce unexpected light touch input.

Teach all of the students in a classroom to stand at arm's length from one another when walking or standing in line.

Allow the individual to stand at the front or back of the line when transitioning between classrooms in the school. Standing in the front of the line allows the student space in front and a visual line of sight. Standing at the back of the line allows the student to see where his or her classmates are positioned and can reduce anxiety of bumping into others.

Provide students with extra time to transition between classes.

Position student away from sources of light, such as facing away from the windows in a classroom.

Teach students to shield eyes when transitioning to outdoors or in harsh lighting.

Cover fluorescent lights with a cover to reduce harsh light.

Remove light bulb from overhead light directly above the student's desk.

 Writing Sensory Diet

Trial writing tool alternatives: pencil grips, pencils of with different levels of hardness, felt-tip pens, ball-point pens, or vibrating pens.

Use a modified writing style of instruction such as Loops and Other Groups writing program (Benbow, 1990).

Provide graph paper for journal work or written answers.

Writing surface alternatives to the desk surface: clipboard, dry erase board, blotters, slant surface, sandpaper, layers of paper, raised-line paper, or textured paper.

Provide worksheets and writing papers with modified spaces for answers: highlighted spaces, bold lines, or boxes.

Allow more time for note taking and fine motor activities, oral tests, writing alternatives (e.g., word processor).

Provide dycem to stabilize papers.

School Break Time (Down Time) Sensory Diet

Utilize brain break activities during times of transition and down time: donkey kicks, heavy marching, pushing against the wall, doorway pushes, "popcorn" activity in chair (popping up at different speeds or intervals), seat exercises, jumping, yoga, hopping, squeezes, stretches, self-imposed body hugs, chair push-ups, wall push-ups, sit-ups, jumping jacks, wheelbarrow walks, crab walking, marching in place, games with clapping patterns using speed and rhythm; jumping, hopping, skipping, or galloping.

Incorporate sensory-rich errands into the child's classroom jobs: carrying heavy books, moving chairs, carrying materials to other classrooms, pushing a supply cart, moving gym mats, or delivering printed materials.

Utilize a routine that provides these activities before class and throughout the day.

Provide frequent breaks during the day.

Recess Sensory Diet

Teach the child to ask if they can push another child on the swing.

Utilize the sensory diet strategies listed under "playground sensory diet".

Organize one-on-one play with a buddy.

Allow use of a weighted tool or fidget tool during recess.

Gym Class Sensory Diet

Consult with the physical education teacher about child's needs and continual activity modification to enhance motor planning.

Consider adding movement and multi-sensory components including clapping games while reciting jingles, foot-to-foot bicycling, jump rope activities, dancing, swimming and pool activities, ball activities.

Simplify sports activities to address motor planning and coordination needs.

Encourage simplified physical education activities; provide visual, auditory, and physical cues.

Encourage the child to participate in heavy work activities such as push-ups, sit-ups, jumping jacks, wheelbarrow walks, or animal walks before and in gym class.

Minimize touch contact with other children when engaged in physical education activities.

Encourage active resistance and joint compression activities before class.

Limit the number of children and space around the child to increase sense of security.

Play Sensory Diet

Utilize the sensory strategies itemized and listed under Special Interest Themed Sensory Diets to encourage highly motivating sensory input through the child's primary occupation of play.

Consider the natural proprioceptive input of aspects of play: roughhousing, play wrestling, leap frog, tug-of-war, wheelbarrow walking, jumping on a small trampoline, crawling under couch cushions, chin-ups, play with weighted balls, jumping and crashing on the bed, pushing another child on the swing, playing in a body sock, foot-to-foot bicycling with friend, and firm family hugging.

Encourage use of tactile and proprioceptive play activities.

Provide containers to organize and hold items that need opening, lifting, and carrying play materials and toys.

Consider the natural vestibular input aspects of play: jumping on a trampoline; playing on slides, swings, seesaws, trapezes, rings, ladders, monkey bars, gliders, and suspended bridges.

Provide a large, open area with unbreakable items for roughhouse play.

Provide "crash areas" in the play space with mattresses, pillows, and beanbag chairs.

Provide options such as an outdoor swing set, indoor suspended swing, mini-trampoline, or community playground.

Use a visual or written list of play options to organize the child who is overwhelmed by choices.

Provide opportunities for pressure and resistance: rolling up with a blanket to make a hot dog or burrito, rolling a large ball over the child to make a pizza, playing tug-of-war, crawling under couch cushions, using a chin-up bar, or crawling into a stretchy body pillow case that has been cut at both ends.

Teach family members about the child's sensory needs and the need to avoid unwanted touch.

Chores Sensory diet

Use chores as a time for sensory input. Most household and classroom "jobs" require heavy work, motor planning, visual processing, integration, and processing of all of the sensory systems in an interconnected manner. Using chores as a sensory strategy is smart!

Household chores can be completed using a family schedule, integrating the chores that need to be completed each week the child's sensory needs.

Heavy work chores like carrying laundry baskets or pushing a vacuum provide proprioception. Sweeping provides vestibular input. There are infinite tasks that can be done around the home or classroom that are sensory goldmines.

Consider proprioceptive input provided naturally during chores: stirring, rolling/kneading dough, digging, carrying, shoveling, raking, pushing/lifting heavy objects, moving furniture, vacuuming, sweeping, mopping, carrying laundry basket.

If morning routines are a challenge, add a daily chore that involves the heavy work of carrying a laundry basket of clothes or moving chairs at the table before completing challenging sensory tasks such as getting dressed.

Avoid chores with breakable items, such as putting away dishes.

QUICK TIP: Have a short list of one-minute chores that can be completed at any given time. These might include jobs like a quick decluttering of a room, gathering garbage bags, or carrying laundry to the washing machine. A chore chart to keep track of these one-minute chores as well as a reward chart is quite effective in providing sensory input with consistent carryover. When the task is a job that everyone in the house needs to participate in on a daily basis, it becomes an ingrained part of the day.

Snacks and Meals Sensory Diet

Provide healthy, chewy foods (e.g., celery, carrots, apples, fruit leather), thick liquids requiring straw (e.g., milkshakes, smoothies, gelatin) for calming input.

Provide crunchy and alerting foods to "wake up" the individual.

Provide heavy work before meals.

Provide a sturdy chair with arms for meals.

Provide deep pressure techniques before meals.

Teach the child to stimulate oral-motor proprioception by biting down hard and releasing, pursing lips and releasing, sucking in cheeks, flapping tongue, blowing balloons, and clicking the tongue.

Provide thick liquids to drink with straw.

Provide a supportive chair or seating system that allows child's feet to touch floor.

Experiment with different utensils such as plastic, rubber coated, weighted, or swivel.

Explore different textures acceptable to the child and reinforce those textured foods for nutrient intake.

Arts and Crafts Sensory Diet

Allow a variety of tactile art media, with alternative options for tactile defensiveness.

Provide a glue stick instead of glue or paste, paintbrush instead of finger paints, and tools to prevent hand use during tactile projects.

Provide heavy work prior to art class.

Allow oral motor chew tools while the child is working on art projects.

Riding the Bus Sensory Diet

Provide a weighted backpack at the proper weight for the child, weighted vest, or heavy jacket.

Ensure the child has own seat, is first or last in line to board bus, and wears headphones to filter out extraneous sensory stimuli.

Create a routine of calming sensory input activities before the bus ride such as gross motor activities, slow rocking, heavy work, joint compression, active resistance activities, or deep breathing exercises.

Allow the child to wear compression garments.

Allow the child to wear their backpack on the front of their body while sitting on the bus.

Provide headphones to minimize stimuli.

Dressing Sensory Diet

Provide deep touch pressure to limbs and torso before and during dressing.

Apply body hugs and hand squeezes.

Determine whether baggy, loose-fitting clothing is preferable and provide those options.

Pre-wash clothing to reduce "itchy" feeling of clothing.

Cut out labels and tags.

Provide seamless clothing and undergarments

Wear socks inside out to avoid seams at the toes.

Provide loose clothing and loose layers to avoid a sense of becoming overheated.

Bathing Sensory Diet

Apply a firm massage prior to and after bath.

Apply a towel wrapped tightly after bath with heavy hugs.

After the bath, firmly apply lotion.

Experiment with different sponges, wash mitts, cloths.

Allow the child to use a soft washing mitt to bathe themselves.

Grooming Sensory Diet

Apply deep pressure prior to hair care or nail cutting.

Encourage use of a weighted blanket worn during nail cutting or hair brushing tasks.

Utilize conditioner and detangle spray.

Trial various combs and brushes. A "wet brush" or soft-bristled hairbrush can help.

Soak the fingernails before cutting.

Try using infant fingernail cutters even with older children.

Tooth Care Sensory Diet

Provide deep pressure activities before brushing teeth, including use of a water pick, textured gum brush, or gum massage input.

When visiting the dentist, provide calming deep pressure techniques while in the dentist's chair. Ask to wear the weighted x-ray blanket during teeth cleaning procedures.

Experiment with different grades and types of toothbrushes.

It can be effective to use a vibrating electric toothbrush.

Consider using a washcloth with toothpaste at first for the child who is sensitive to brushing.

Sleep and Bedtime Routine Sensory Diet

Incorporate deep pressure hugs and slow rocking into the pre-bedtime routine.

Require no roughhousing and TV before bedtime.

Use a heavy blanket such as a duvet or weighted blanket made for the child's weight.

Create a calming bedtime routine before bedtime including massage, stretches or yoga, joint compression, or slow rocking.

Provide prewashed soft sheets.

Try using a sleeping bag.

Consider placing the bed mattress on the floor.

Difficult Transition Periods of the Day

Each of the periods of the day described below are those that have requirements for transition from task to task with a functional end-result; Getting out the door, participating in a meal, functioning in the school day, shopping in a store, or bedtime all have a specific task or tasks that need to be accomplished. These transition periods can be a time of sensory meltdown.

The strategies below describe sensory components that are integrated into the child's day as opposed to added sensory activities.

Morning - The rush of morning routines including getting the individual with sensory needs out of bed, dressed, fed, groomed, and out the door with all of the necessary extras (bookbags, shoes, jackets, cold-weather accessories, and other items) can be a time of struggle, particularly if there are sensory challenges to overcome. Waking up, bathroom issues, picky eating, routine changes, clothing sensitivities, tooth care, and challenges with brushing hair all play into the puzzle of puzzles that was discussed in an earlier chapter.

• Sensory needs can be addressed by carrying heavy items first thing in the morning.
• Move furniture to get increased proprioceptive input, such as moving a bin of clothing or laundry basket to gather needed items for the day.
• Incorporate a morning exercise routine that includes push-ups, sit-ups, running in place, jumping jacks, toe touches, or other gross motor and heavy work tasks.
• Allow the child to jump on a trampoline before getting ready for the day.
• Using the child's sensory preferences, provide modified clothing including compression shirts, seamless socks or clothing, Velcro shoes, etc.
• The use of weighted blankets or compression bed sheets can have a calming impact on the beginning of the day.
• Utilize adaptive seating

during meals.
• Trial a visual routine for morning activities.

Meals - Mealtime is a hectic time of the day for many families. After a long day, sitting down at the table is oftentimes a difficult element to fit into busy schedules. Adding sensory components within the family mealtime can be an effective strategy for the sensory family.

• Allow use of adaptive seating including cushions, therapy band on chairs, or sitting on a partially deflated beach ball.
• Allow the child with sensory needs a break during meals to get up and walk around. Use a timer or visual schedule to bring the child back to the table. Or, consider allowing a walk-around meal where the child can stand and eat within a certain area.
• Provide chewy foods or crunchy foods to meet sensory needs within the family meal.
• Allow use of a straw to provided added proprioceptive input to drinks or soups.
• Consider previous movement and sensory requirements of the child: If the child has returned home from a long day of sitting at school, allow a movement or sensory break

before the meal.
• When preparing foods, add foods that provide proprioceptive input through oral motor and deep pressure. Proprioception and tactile input are deeply connected and can be considered during food selection for the sensory child. Consider adding crunch to a smooth meal. Add croutons to soups. Add granola to oatmeal. Add crunchy cereal to yogurt. Add chewy raisins to cookies. Add fruit chunks to oatmeal.

Social Situations (parties, events, holiday celebrations) - Consider the sensory challenges that we experience at a birthday party or special event; There are new and unique smells, balloons popping, the closeness of people in a crowded event, others bumping into you, and unpredictable events. It is a scene high in sensory input. For the individual with sensory processing issues or those who cannot regulate sensory input, responses can be difficult to manage.

Sensory diet activities can be incorporated into social situations:

• Use a travel sensory kit.
• Use calming strategies including deep pressure, joint compressions, and heavy work.
• Allow extra space around the individual with sensory needs.
• Provide frequent movement breaks.

• Prepare a calm-down space in an extra bedroom, in the car, or during an outdoor walk.

After-School - The afternoon period of transitioning from a long day of sitting in a classroom to a time of freedom and a space where one feels comfortable and safe can result in overstimulation for some individuals or under-stimulation for others.

The after-school hours may involve homework, parents helping siblings with homework assignments, dinner preparations, and evening activity schedules to attend to. Parents and siblings are also at a tiring point in the day and may struggle to regulate sensory input and emotions.

Sensory diet activities can be incorporated into the after-school time period:

• Allow homework to be completed while standing or walking around.
• Provide a sensory after-school snack.
• Utilize movement breaks more frequently if indicated.
• Try yoga stretches or deep breathing breaks during and within after-school

transitions.
• Use a visual schedule to indicate after-school and evening schedules

---

Homework Time - Asking a child with sensory needs to sit and perform homework after attending during a long school day can result in breakdowns. Incorporate sensory adjustments and input into the homework time for better results:

• Use modified writing utensils (vibrating pen, mechanical pencil, soft-lead pencil, crayons, or wax pencils).
• Use modified paper (highlighted lines, bold lines, raised lined paper, graph paper, or writing areas with boxed spaces for writing individual letters).
• Reduce the amount of writing required.
• Allow worksheets or assignments to be transcribed.
• Add movement breaks into homework tasks.
• Provide a calming or stimulating snack or drink during homework.
• Reduce distractions and provide a specified homework space.

Pre-bedtime - Wrapping up the day and getting children into pajamas and settled down can be a difficult transition after a long and busy day of sensory challenges. Use sensory strategies to make this transition easier:

• Use a soft-bristled toothbrush for brushing teeth.
• End the day with a story time under a weighted blanket.
• Use a heated blanket to calm down.
• Use a visual schedule of pre-bedtime events
• Use a timer or adapted clock to provide a visual for evening events.

Bedtime (sleep) - The act of settling down and falling asleep can be a challenge for the individual with sensory processing issues. Children hear noises as the house settles. They hear others in the home who are still awake. They see shadows in their bedroom. They feel the blanket or stuffed animals in their bed and can focus only on those sensations. Bedtime is a time when the interoceptive system can become intensified and children can feel their heart pounding, their belly rumbling as the digestive system works, and experience the release of chemicals that result in hyper-alertness. Proprioceptive and tactile input can be a calming tool to address alertness, awareness, and discrimination issues at bedtime.

Sensory diet changes to make at bedtime:

• Use a weighted blanket or heavy

comforter.
- Use tight and fitted compression sheets.
- Provide weighted stuffed animals.
- Try scented stuffed animals or blankets scented with calming scents.
- Use massage with lotion prior to bed.
- Ty joint compressions before bed.
- Try meditation and deep breathing before bed.
- Use calming music before bed.
- Use blackout shades in the bedroom.
- Trial use of a nightlight or a string of Christmas lights for a low light in the bedroom.
- Use a low ceiling light or sensory lights at night.
- Use an adapted alarm clock for a low-stimulation wake-up.

Community Outings - When out in the community, self-regulation can be a detriment to completing functional tasks such as shopping, navigating the public library, utilizing public transportation, or attending functions. The opportunity for a sensory breakdown is high.

When the daily tasks require several stops the grocery store, post office, library, and other stops, it can be helpful to include a movement break into the routine. A timed 20-minute stop at the playground can provide alerting or calming sensory input to meet a vast variety of needs.

Consider the playground and its natural environment for encouraging sensory input:

Swings- Full body movements can be developed through gravitational insecurity on the swings. Lying in a prone (superman) position on the swings is organizing in a forward/back motion on the swings. Slow swinging in the prone position helps to normalize a child with tactile defensiveness.

- Encourage the child to look up in front of them and even toss bean bags into a bucket. Ask the child to notice things around them in the playground area and play games like "I Spy" while slowly swinging back and forth in the prone position.
- Spinning on playground swings requires strength of the arms and upper body to maintain an upright position. The vestibular stimulation received from spinning is intense and shouldn't be utilized for more than 10 minutes.
- Position the child sideways in the swing so the swings are straddling the seat of the swing. Children can then be slowly pushed side to side as well as front-to-back.

Slide - Riding down a slide promotes use of position in space as the child holds themselves up against the pull of gravity.

- Another idea for using the slide for sensory input is to have the child lay prone on the slide without movement.

Use the upward ramp of the slide as a positioner for art creation or eye-hand coordination games like rolling a tennis ball up the slide and catching it as it rolls back down.

• Walking and crawling up the slides while looking upward is a test of gravity while encouraging bilateral coordination and core body strength.

Tunnels - Encourage crawling and scooting through playground tunnels with eyes up and looking out of the tunnel so that the child's head and neck are resisting gravity and vision is guiding movement.

Merry-go-round - Spinning on a merry-go-round can be done in a seated, prone, or supine position. Holding onto the bars and maintaining upright posture is a strengthening exercise and a source of proprioceptive input.

Balance Beam - Balance beams can be used in obstacle courses and are a great source of vestibular and proprioceptive input while encouraging visual changes. Show the child how to look up forward as they walk along a balance beam.

Steps - Many playground equipment sets have small sets of steps to reach different levels. Children can climb the steps, using the banister for support if needed. Try having the child pull themselves up the steps using the banister for a change in body and head position that promotes proprioceptive input, using the body's weight against gravity.

Picnic Bench - Lying prone on the seat of the picnic bench while the hands are dropped to the ground is a way to work against gravity through the arms in a ball tossing game, or drawing in the dirt with a stick. Ask the child to scoot forward on the bench so that they need to work harder for efficiency of the vestibular system and against gravity. This type of activity promotes use of the eyes in an activity while the back, arms, head, and neck are used against gravity and help to build visual perception.

Vertical Ladder - Climbing a ladder to monkey bars requires strength, bilateral coordination, and provides vestibular input. Using the child's own body weight is effective in providing proprioceptive input. Children can look up with neck extension to further adjust vestibular receptor response to movement in space.

Ramps - Many playgrounds have ramps built in within the playground. Crawling, scooting, walking toe-to-toe, and sliding up and down these ramps provide many different sensory input opportunities. Try rolling a ball up or down these ramps into a target or to a friend.

All of these strategies are guides that can use sensory input to create a sensory lifestyle, integrating sensory input into naturally occurring tasks within the child's day. In this way, sensory input becomes authentic and meaningful. Be sure to utilize sensory activities that address the child's specific needs.

Chapter 7
Special Interest Sensory Diets

We all have interests, likes, dislikes, and hobbies. These interests are what makes us who we are. A sensory diet that is designed around a specific interest is an occupation-based tool for children who struggle to participate in general sensory tasks. While therapeutic activities are designed to be fun and engaging, a sensory activity that hits on a desired theme is one that is motivating and beneficial in more ways than just the benefit of important sensory input. A child who struggles to participate in activities that challenge his or her sensory system is more likely to tolerate a themed sensory diet when it seems like playing with his favorite toys.

A list of favorite sensory activities based on a special interest can take the benefits of a sensory diet to the next level of participation. The child with sensory needs can use their individually-designed themed sensory diet to tolerate even more sensations, maximize attention and integration, understand self-regulation strategies, improve self-esteem and self-confidence, tolerate social situations, and move from defensive states of activity to accept situations.

A sensory diet can be the tool that helps kids with sensory processing issues to function in an appropriate way in every environment. A special interest sensory diet is one component that provides a selection of motivating sensory options in a specific time period (such as in the classroom) or throughout the day. These special interest sensory diet items may be scheduled or may be provided as choices in a child's day. Utilizing special interests as a guide for creating a sensory diet is motivating and authentic. It's a step toward solving the puzzle that is meeting a child's sensory needs in an intrinsic manner.

How can sensory diets be incorporated into special themes based on the interest of the child?

First, let's talk about interests. Interest is a defined as a psychological state of engagement, both directly and ongoing. Interest is a predisposition to engage repeatedly with particular ideas, events, or objects over time. Interests promote feelings of attention, concern, or curiosity creating a period of engagement by a thing, person, object, place, theme, or idea.

There have been studies that indicate passionate interests can allow individuals to overcome academic difficulties or perceptual difficulties. Given interest-guided opportunities, a child has various motivations for learning (Jones & Nimmo 1994). Using interests as a sensory tool may potentially improve carryover, motivation, and interaction with special-themed sensory activities.

Using a sensory diet that is specifically designed to meet the needs of a child's interests can especially help children who is challenged by motivation.

It is essential to understand that every child's sensory needs, challenges, and strengths differ from others. So, why should they follow a cookie cutter sensory diet as a therapeutic tool?

Using play as a tactic for introducing sensory strategies is meaningful and authentic. When used as a means for sensory diet activities, play can potentially impact carryover and motivation with sensory diet activities.

Play is intrinsically motivating for children. If children are participating in activity that they do not enjoy, then it is not play. It's work. At its basic level, individuals participate in play simply for the satisfaction. Play is individualized, meaning that each individual is motivated by their own interests. Play is in itself, the process of physical and/or mental activity, sometimes with acting out imaginary themes. Play is voluntary and many times, spontaneous, either individually or with others (Krasnor & Pepler, 1980; Rubin, Fein, & Vandenberg, 1983). These criteria make play what it is - Fun!

There are several questions that can be asked about making sensory diet activities intrinsically motivating in play:

* Can sensory diet activities revolve around play in a way that does not take away from the underlying criteria that make up "play"?

* Can sensory activities be presented in a way that is not only rewarding intrinsically, but meaningful and authentic?

* Can sensory diet tasks be provided in a manner that is process oriented, pleasurable, and freely chosen?

If the connection between needed sensory input and individualized interests can be combined, there is a real opportunity for successful self-regulation and modulation of sensory input in all environments.

Using a specific, themed based sensory diet can meet the needs of the child with sensory processing disorder as a motivator. Kids who struggle with sensory issues will be encouraged to participate in activities that fall under their interests. The child who loves to play with trains will want to engage in sensory activities that involve trains. Even activities that are challenging can become more interesting with the desired theme is incorporated.

Each child has their own personality and special talents. These interests and strengths should be emphasized in addition to addressing learning challenges or goal areas.

A child's greatest achievements are possible in play, achievements that tomorrow will become her basic level of real action. — Lev Vygotsky

A Warning About Special Interest Sensory Diets

There are a couple of items to consider when introducing a child to special interest sensory diets. Above all, it is essential to recognize that each child processes sensory information uniquely. Children with very similar sensory responses and resulting behaviors may respond completely different to the same structured sensory diet. Although the treatment techniques and the associated sensory diet suggestions described in this book are recommended, it is imperative that individualized assessment of each child occurs

in order to discern whether these measures are appropriate. Additionally, an occupational therapist, along with the individual's family and team should monitor the child's responsiveness to the strategies in each performance context in order to determine effectiveness. Adverse responses indicate a need to adjust interventions and modify the treatment approach accordingly (Koomar & Bundy, 1991).

Many times, a sensory activity may work in one environment but not another. Every functional task should be assessed with regard to environmental input and performance context.

The child who is initially thrilled by a specific theme may become bored or "over" the themed activity when they are presented with daily activities based on their interest. This may be a result of over-exposure or it may become a resulting behavior following sensory challenges that are threatening or too much for the child with sensory issues.

How to set up a Special Interest Sensory Diet

Think about the activities that your child is most interested in. What is the one thing that keeps your child centered and focused. There may be different activities, toys, games, or even television shows that your child is especially interested in. Whatever the area, it is possible to incorporate special interests into a motivating and successful sensory lifestyle.

Interventions can address sensory needs as well as incorporating preferred sensory input. Keep in mind that all of the sensory systems are connected and together allow an individual to perceive his environment. Consider the vestibular sensory system that is deeply connected to the auditory system and inner ear workings. Other sensory systems work together in the same area but impact our perception differently. Taste/ gustatory sensation and proprioception of the mouth appear in the same area, but are intertwined with other sensory systems. The oral system's tongue, inside of the cheeks, and palate are all impacted by tactile input. However, the ability to chew, suck, blow, puff the cheeks, clench the jaw, purse the lips, and make facial expressions are oral motor components. These actions require joints and muscles and activate the proprioceptive system.

Calming and alerting sensory strategies can be incorporated into any theme, touching on a child's special interests. Use the guide in the following chapter to meet the needs of any child while addressing unmet sensory needs.

Back in chapter one, we talked about the concept of a play being a child's primary occupation. While sensory diet strategies should be incorporated into a lifestyle of sensory needs, the idea of adding therapeutic sensory input into play is a valuable one. Utilizing the primary occupation of play as a vessel for sensory diet strategies can be very motivating. The sensory diet becomes meaningful. It becomes integrated naturally. The ability to ensure carryover of sensory diet techniques is more consistent when integrated within play-based interests.

The activities in this chapter are a guide designed to follow a themed special interest.

These activities are broken down into sections based on sensory need. Remember that each child's sensory needs differ and certain sensory activities will benefit some children but not others. Use the activities as a guide based on the child's specific needs. Consider that some activities may work one day but not the next day. Activities can be done in a general manner or with an added component making them a highly motivating themed "game" for children.

The child who loves trains can add a toy train to sensory activities or pretend the heavy work activities are part of an imaginary scenario where trains push a load up tracks. The child who loves dolls can perform activities with a doll

friend or in order to help their doll. The imaginary scenarios are infinite. Use the sensory program outlined in this book to identify activities to use in a sensory-based daily schedule and then add in special interest themed components. Activities should be based on establishing daily input as well as meeting goals or needs.

When creating a play-based sensory diet, utilize favorite interests and themes. These activities can be incorporated naturally into transitions, occupations, and various environments to create a sensory lifestyle.

Using a Themed Special Interest Checklist in Sensory Diet Development

Use the Themed Special Interest Checklist in the Addendum section of this book to identify specific special interests based on topic area. This can be a valuable tool to identify additional areas of interest that can be used in creating a preferred sensory diet activity. Interest-based sensory diet activities can be powerful in carryover for the child with sensory needs.

Consider how each interest can be developed into a themed and motivating sensory diet.

Calming Themed Activities

Kids can learn to use the calming strategies below to "let off steam" when they need to calm down. Using the activities below in a daily schedule can help kids to incorporate the sensory input before it's needed.

Sensory Activities	Special Interest Ideas
Push a large cardboard box or laundry basket filled with heavy items.	Invite the child to pretend they are pushing a train/toy/doll/other pretend play characters. Take the activity outside and push the box/basket up and down hills. Fill with items of interest such as blocks or toys.
Draw train tracks/road on a piece of paper. Use a kneaded eraser to erase the tracks.	A basket or box can be a construction vehicle. Use the basket as a dump truck to dump out heavy items. An eraser (moldable or rectangular school eraser) can be a vehicle for small play figures.
Draw train tracks on sandpaper. Try laying a piece of paper on top of sandpaper. Draw train tracks on the paper.	Push wooden 2x4 cut pieces of wood on a sidewalk or driveway. To increase resistance and make the task more difficult, add wrap sandpaper around the wooden block. You can find scraps of wood at many hardware centers. Pretend play figures can "ride" on the wooden piece.
Take a warm bath.	Add interest components-stick letters to the wall, add floating mat with toys, bubbles with a bubble wand. Add floating foam letters or foam sheets to hold water-safe toys.
Tape "tracks" on the carpet using masking tape. Kids can push furniture along the tracks.	Push dolls, stuffed animals, cars, dump trucks, toy garbage truck on the tracks.

Pop bubble wrap.	The bubbles are train coal, fairy clouds, unicorn pillows, doll stepping stones. Use your imagination to add favorite interest components. Make a game for children who like to throw a ball. Make a bubble wrap hopscotch game. Create a bubble wrap ball by tightly rolling bubble wrap and taping it into a ball.
Massage with or without lotion.	Read a favorite story during a deep pressure massage. Always keep one hand on the child's body during the massage. Teach kids how to massage their hands with deep pressure between their fingers and in the palm.
Provide therapy brushing.	Tell a themed story during the brushing. Talk in low and calm voice. Use caution with brushing and perform this sensory activity under the supervision of an occupational therapist.
Try log rolling.	Pretend to be explorers, rolling dolls, steam rollers, etc. as children roll across the room for movement and rotary sensory stimulation.
Encourage tumbling.	Invent a story based on the child's special interest. Roll and tumble as part of the story.
Make a DIY weighted blanket by stuffing a duvet with several heavy blankets. A weighted lap pillow would work in this manner as well.	Draw or paint train tracks on the blanket cover with permanent fabric markers or paint. The child can sit under the blanket and drive trains over the tracks. Use favorite colors or themed character sheets to create a special interest blanket.
Swaddle the child with blankets.	Use a favorite blanket and stuffed animals to roll the child up tightly in a blanket. Pretend to be part of a special interest story or game.
Give bear hugs.	Hugs can come from a parent or children can be taught self-hugging. Call the bear hugs another name like a favorite animal or character like a doll or an action figure.
Provide a stuffed toy, filled with weighted material (filler beads, dry beans, rice, etc.)	Stuff a themed pillow case that matches the child's interests

Utilize hand fidget tools.	Create a special interest fidget box decorated with special interest themed stickers.
Give a back rub.	Apply a calming back rub with deep pressure. Incorporate music and rhythm for a multi-sensory calming experience. Back rubs can be a bedtime routine that is worked into the nightly schedule to calm children down before bedtime. Add story time or storytelling to incorporate a child's interests.
Provide joint compressions.	Joint compressions can be a powerful calming strategy for children. Activation of the joint receptors provides a deep joint calming sensation. Incorporate special interests by creating a themed song or story that involves repetitions of joint compression.
Scrub the child with a washcloth.	Tactile sensory input can be applied through a washcloth that meets the individual textural preferences of the child. Add warm soapy water and "bathe" favorite toys at the same time as the child.
Encourage warm water play.	Waterplay can occur in the bathtub, at a kitchen sink, or in a large plastic bin. Add plastic toys such as dolls, dinosaurs, cars, etc. that meet the individual's preferences.
Wear compression fabrics under clothing.	Garments can be provided in the child's preferred color or with branding. Consider using a smaller size swim shirt that comes in short or long-sleeved styles. Consider using a smaller sized athletic wear in lycra or spandex. These versions of compression fabrics often are available in at a less expensive cost and in a variety of themes and colors.
"Sandwich" the child between pillows.	Add couch cushions and pillows to pretend play. Compression between cushions provides heavy input that is calming to the proprioceptive and tactile systems. Favorite toys can be sandwiched between cushions along with the child.

Climb under the sofa cushions.	Create a pretend play obstacle course right in the living room using cushions and pillows.
Use play dough, slime, floam, kinetic sand, Silly Putty, or clay.	Add small toys to play dough or other sensory dough experiences. Allowing doughs to harden in the room air can provide a greater resistance to the hands and upper extremities. Another idea is to freeze doughs for a temperature experience. Freezing sensory doughs provides a greater resistance to the hands while the dough is hardened.
Create a sensory bin with dry rice & beans or other materials.	Add favorite toys to dry sensory bins or sensory tables. Incorporate favorite themes.
Encourage the child to help with gardening.	Use a variety of digging tools or gardening tools while gaining proprioceptive input in the garden. Children can help to plant favorite foods, and then help with harvesting and food preparation. Encourage children to get down on the ground on all fours when planting and weeding garden crops.
Provide vibrating toys - pens, balls, stuffed toys.	There are many options for toys and tools that include a vibrating portion including pens and toothbrushes. Provide these tools as a sensory tool by adding themed stickers to meet the child's interests. Stuffed toys and animals can be used within interests or in games and activities.
Use a vibrating toothbrush.	Add a favorite sticker to vibrating toothbrush for use in oral hygiene or as an additional tool for sensory input.
Jump on a "crash pad".	Add favorite soft, plush stuffed animals or toys to a crash area. The child can jump and crash gaining sensory input.
Pet a dog, cat, or other animal.	A pet can create an option for tactile sensory input and proprioceptive input when lying with a child. Incorporate animal needs such as walks into the child's day as a means for vestibular and proprioceptive input. Children can help to care for the pet by carrying heavy food bags and water for the family pet while gaining organizing sensory input.

Encourage the child to participate in cooking tasks.	Invite the child to participate in cooking tasks while creating meals for the family while participating in calming sensory input by cutting, chopping, lifting, washing, drying, and rolling.
Provide a weighted blanket, vest, or lap pad.	A homemade weighted lap pad or weighted blanket can be created using themed materials or favorite colors. Be sure to utilize appropriate weight requirements according to the child's weight.
Roll the child up in a "burrito" blanket.	Incorporate proprioceptive input from a blanket or heavy blanket into play using themed blankets or sheets.
Encourage rocking in an adult's arms, on a toy such as a hobby horse, or in a rocking chair.	Listening to favorite songs or watching a favorite show, movie, or reading a book can be completed with a calming rocking movement.
Play "horse" on an adult's knee.	Playing "horse" with an adult can be a favorite game. The adult can hold the child on their knee, challenging the child's balance at various speeds as the adult raises and lowers their supporting leg.
Play Row, Row, Row Your Boat on an adult's knee or lap.	Challenge balance and core strength with gross motor games at various speeds.
Crawl on the hands and knees.	Incorporate crawling into obstacle course games or in play with a themed interest such as with tunnels and favorite toys.
Army crawl with the child's full body on the floor.	Add proprioceptive input to a crawling obstacle course with favorite toys and themes.
Perform wall push-ups.	Utilize stickers on the wall to indicate a space for wall push-ups. These can be incorporated into obstacle courses or part of a daily routine.
Perform chair push-ups.	Incorporate chair push-ups into the classroom, school lunch room, or bus rides. Chair push-ups are a good class-wide activity for incorporated movement into learning or use as a brain break activity.
Perform yoga exercises.	Utilize themed positions based on animals, sports, or characters that incorporated calming yoga positioning.

Push, pull, or stack toys or household objects.	Utilize boxes or milk crates to hold materials in the classroom or favorite toys. The child can use the bins as a storage system that needs to be moved each day as part of a routine.
Encourage the child to lie on their stomach during writing and reading tasks.	Create a specified space for the individual child depicted by a themed or favorite name. Writing in the prone position allows for calming sensory input through the upper body. A special space for reading or writing can be a motivating factor for some children.
Work in a cocooned environment.	A special place such as a sleeping bag, fabric tube, or body sock such as a mermaid's tail or shark's tail can have a calming effect on some children.
Create a tent or cardboard box calm down area.	A special space such as an enclosed tent, cardboard box, fabric-covered fort, or corner of the room is a calming space for children with sensory needs. Allow the child to utilize adapted seating systems or visual input as indicated. Low lighting, lava lamps, sensory lights, or nightlights can be a visual component for some children.
Drink from a water bottle with straw.	Utilize a sports bottle or water bottle with a straw for calming oral proprioceptive input. Add favorite stickers, colors, or themed additions to the water bottle options.
Hang from the monkey bars.	Utilize playground equipment such as monkey bars or overhead bars as a way to include proprioceptive input into play. Include these components into obstacle courses and learning courses. Indoor options include bars that can be hung from beams or in doorways.
Push the desk/chairs/furniture against walls.	Utilize the furniture into classroom organizing input for the child who likes to "help" in the morning and evening of the school day. Include this job into a daily schedule.

Wear a weighted backpack worn for 15-20 minutes with an hour in between each trial.	Utilize a weighted backpack or front pack in a favorite color or theme. Be sure to utilize properly adjusted weight requirements based on the child's weight. Posture and positioning with a backpack must be considered.
Encourage rocking in song and dance.	Utilize favorite songs into calming rocking positioning and movement.
Provide warmth.	Allow a favorite sweatshirt or other clothing to be worn, utilizing favorite colors, teams, or themes.
Encourage rhythmic movement.	Add calming motions into walks down a hallway, as a centering action when moving from a stimulating environment, or before/during/after transitions. Add a favorite song or incorporate a rhyme into the rhythmic motions.
Provide soft and calm music.	Add favorite song options to a playlist available in the classroom or in a calm-down spot. Use these songs during transitions or car rides.
Dim the lights.	Use low lights in areas of the classroom or home, using themed or favorite color lamps or shades.
Encourage the Superman pose in play.	Incorporate the superman pose into play, games, or learning. Children who are interested in super heroes or mythical characters can use this pose in play or in brain-breaks.
Sit on carpet squares and scoot across the floor.	Use a square of carpet scraps as a movement break or in obstacle courses and learning courses. Add favorite and themed components to the brain break activity or play.
Provide a bungee cord across feet of a chair.	Tie a string of bungee cord or therapy band across the feet of a classroom chair or dining room chair. Use the feet to add movement during periods when the child should sit for a period of time.
Encourage heavy touch pressure.	Include heavy input through the shoulders or legs as part of a massage during bedtime routines. Sing a favorite calming song while applying heavy tough pressure.
Provide chewy snacks.	Include a snack pack that has chewy snacks

Carry the groceries.	Allow the child to carry heavy grocery bags during shopping trips. The child can have their own labelled grocery bag or a specific bag.

Alerting Themed Activities

Children can use the alerting sensory activities to "wake up" the sensory systems and become more alert and attentive.

Sensory Activities	Special Interest Ideas
Dance together.	Use favorite music or themed songs from shows or movies as a movement and brain break activity that alerts and "wakes-up" the child. Incorporate a variety of positions into movements.
Provide movement routines such as walking, running, jumping, and marching.	Provide a transition movement routine for periods of moving between classrooms or when entering/leaving the home. Use a favorite game, movie, television show, or song as inspiration. Add inverted head positioning into the movement routine.
Do the Bunny Hop.	Add dancing and hopping into transition periods. Include competitive potions if the child is interested by this aspect.
Do a wheelbarrow walk.	Use the inverted positioning and whole-body movement of wheelbarrow racing into obstacle races and transitions. The child can is a favorite toy or preferred reward following wheelbarrow racing.
Complete animal walks.	Use favorite animals as a theme for animal walks. A family pet can be a motivating aspect for participating in animal walks. Use various animal walks in races and obstacle courses.

Complete jumping jacks.	Incorporate favorite music and songs into jumping jack activities. Jumping jacks can be a powerful part of a learning activity when combined with learning tasks.
Perform floor push-ups.	Use floor push-ups with preferred songs or music.
Perform chair push-ups.	Incorporate chair push-ups into the classroom for a way to "wake up" the child's body. Add competition aspects or music to the push-up period.
Encourage bike riding.	Add movement and gross motor components of bike riding into obstacle courses or outdoor play
Play on the swings.	They can drive a train car under the swing on the floor. To make this a creative art activity, dip the toy train in paint and ask them to drive the train on a piece of paper as they swing.
Climb up the playground slides.	Add playground equipment into sensory breaks at school or after school routines. A quick stop at a playground can be a motivating part of a daily routine.
Climb up ladders.	Utilize various sized climbing toys and equipment to incorporate imagination games and favorite character stickers to reach various heights. Utilize playground ladders in Simon Says games and obstacle course memory type of games.
Jump on a mini-trampoline.	Use a mini trampoline in dance games or to stand and jump while catching sports balls. Children can use the trampoline surface to play imagination games such as small figures, dolls, matchbox cars, or to complete art activities.
Use a Sit n' Spin, Dizzy Disc Jr, or other spinning toys.	Set up a sensory area with preferred toys amongst spinning sensory toys.
Play with Hop-It balls.	Use hop ball to encourage movement in various directions via obstacle courses and Simon Says games.
Provide inflatable seat cushions.	Utilize inflatable therapy cushions or partially deflated beach ball cushions in activities such as card games, play dough, art and craft creation, board games, and table-top games.

Bounce on a therapy ball.	Utilize a therapy ball during seated game activities including video games or computer games.
Ride a tricycle/bicycle.	Use ride-on toys and bicycles in outdoor play or at playground settings. An exercise bike or foot pedal machine can provide movement input while completing seated games and activities.
Ride a scooter/skateboard.	Use a scooter board or skateboard in game and play activities on the floor, including board games and video game play.
Climb the stairs.	Use the stairs as a means to providing sensory and vestibular input by placing needed items and preferred toys at different levels of the home.
Go swimming.	Encourage movement and participation in multiple plane swimming activities through obstacle courses, Simon Says, the Hokey Pokey, or even 'hopscotch" while in the pool.
Push a grocery cart, stroller, wheelbarrow, or toy with wheels.	Use a small toy stroller, toy grocery cart, toy wheelbarrow to push toys in imagination play. Add weights to the bottom of the toy with ankle weights that can be attached via Velcro. Older children can push these items in yard work or while shopping.
Try Brain Gym exercises.	Incorporate Brain Gym exercises into a daily routine.
Roll down a hill.	Add rolling to an obstacle course or Simon Says type of listening game.
Do the Hokey Pokey.	The Hokey Pokey can be adapted to any theme. Consider Snowman Pokey, Baseball Pokey, Princess Pokey, etc.
Play catch together.	Play catch with any type of ball. Wrist weights can be added for additional proprioceptive input. Make the activity alerting by throwing the ball in various planes. Small balls can also be thrown against a blank wall indoors. Incorporate ball catch games into learning or homework tasks.

Play balloon tennis.	Use a balloon to play tennis, volleyball, catch, or "don't drop the balloon". Incorporate balloon games into learning or homework.
Play hopscotch together.	Play hopscotch indoors or outdoors, using chalk or masking tape to create a board. Children can use a variety of interest-based items to toss onto the board. Incorporate hopscotch into learning or homework tasks.
Do cartwheels and somersaults.	Utilize a large gym mat within the home to encourage somersaults or gymnastics throughout the day, incorporating into homework or learning if needed. Favorite songs can be used.
Go ice skating/sledding/skiing.	Outdoor winter activities can be done during summer months on a grassy hill (Use a piece of cardboard to "sled" down a hill). Use recycled shoeboxes or pieces of wax paper to "ice skate" on a carpet. Include these activities into favorite songs and obstacle courses or learning activities.
Play or sit on a therapy ball.	Children can position themselves on the ball as they drive a toy train on the floor.
Do arm windmills.	Use arm windmill exercises within a morning or bedtime routine, adding favorite music.
Encourage movement rhymes and dances.	Change the lyrics to rhymes like head shoulders knees and toes or Row, Row, Row Your Boat to favorite themes or songs.
Participate in jumping activities and games.	Add favorite music or toys in a jumping obstacle course. Use jumping activities and games in obstacle courses or homework tasks.
Do yoga.	Trial various kids' yoga YouTube channels or obtain yoga videos from the library to use in a morning or bedtime routine. Schedule in yoga as a family activity. Incorporate favorite themes such as animal yoga, sports yoga, etc. Many common yoga positions can be adjusted and called a fun name to meet the special interests of a child.
Dance together.	Encourage dancing to favorite songs.

The calming and sensory activities outlined above are just an example of the variety of methods for incorporating sensory diet into a sensory lifestyle. Consider these sensory diet strategies and how they can be modified to an interest-based sensory diet:

Oral Motor Activities

- Blow a train whistle.
- Use a party blower as a pretend train whistle.
- Make a train themed straw. Cut a small train shape from cardstock. Tape it to a straw. The child can use the straw to blow cotton balls (the train's smoke) across a table. To make this activity more difficult, have the child blow the cotton ball along a length of toy train tracks.
- Provide chewy foods to add heavy work and proprioceptive input through the jaw.
- Provide crunchy foods to alert and increase attention (raw fruits and vegetables, licorice, gummy snacks, pretzel rods, or gum).
- Provide food with intense flavors (sour or salty).
- Suck on hard candy.
- Try Pop Rocks candy.
- Encourage varying textured food.
- Incorporate snacks with a variety of textures including chewy and/or crunchy foods to alert and increase attention.
- Provide snacks and foods intense flavors such as lemon/lime, salt, etc.
- Provide whistle or instruments such as a kazoo
- Blowing activities such as bubbles with a bubble wand, blowing cotton balls across a table surface, making bubbles with a straw in water, etc.
- Provide things to chew on including therapy tubes, chewing necklaces, keychains, pencil toppers, etc. A therapist can provide an appropriate resistance for these items.

Tactile Activities

- Draw "train tracks" on the child's back during a calming back rub. Tracks can go up and down the arms and fingers, too.
- Create a themed bath. Cut small kitchen sponges into rectangles to create. When wet, sponge pieces will stick to the wall of a shower.
- Drive toy trains or cars up and down the child's back, legs, and arms.
- Promote sensory play with a variety of sensory materials such as clay, play dough, slime, or sensory bins.
- Use a vibrating pen to write or draw preferred information or depictions of interest-based drawings.
- Play in sensory bins of dry materials including, but not limited to: dry beans, pasta, rice, sand, pebbles, etc.
- Play in textured materials in a sensory bin or on a table surface with materials such as shaving cream, "goop", slime, wet play dough, water, etc.
- Draw or write in textured surfaces.

Auditory Activities

- Listen to favorite music.
- Discover calming vs. arousing music.
- Bang on pots and pans.
- Play musical instruments.
- Listen to sounds of nature outdoors.
- Sing.
- Hum a song.
- Whisper a secret message.
- Blow whistles.
- Try therapeutic listening programs.
- Use a white noise machine, CD, or app.
- Observe silence.
- Identify and label sounds.
- Use earplugs or sound-canceling headphones.
- Explore the stereo or tablet volume controls.
- Create a "safe space" with quiet and low light.

Visual Activities

- Look at mobiles.
- Use a lava lamp.
- Look at bubble lamps.
- Explore colored lightbulbs.
- Avoid fluorescent bulbs (visual flicker, noise, and mercury content in compact fluorescents).
- Respect color preference in clothing, objects, and interior decorating.
- Reconsider complicated prints and patterns on clothing, walls, and floors.
- Place toys in opaque containers.

- Leave out 5-10 toys at a time to avoid visual overload.
- Look at photos and picture books.

Snacks

Kids can help in the kitchen to prepare foods and snacks. Aspects of food preparation provides calming, proprioceptive input: Peeling vegetables with a hand-held vegetable peeler, cutting with a child-safe knife, using a child-friendly food grater, and washing dishes in warm water are some examples. Use these activities to create themed foods based on the child's interest or simply use themed plates and bowls that are commercially available.

Another way to create themed interests in the

kitchen and during meal time is using a themed mat for food preparation or eating. The child can make their own mat that can then be laminated. Consider adding coloring pages or stickers for cartoon character interests.

Addressing other developmental areas with a sensory diet:

When sensory processing is a challenge for children, it can be common for other areas of development to be delayed or challenged. Incorporating a sensory diet into developmental needs is one way to promote development of areas such as fine motor skills, gross motor skills, or oculomotor function.

Motor Considerations

A sensory diet can include activities that incorporate motor planning and coordination activities. Here are some ideas:

- Use a balance beam.
- Straddle a therapy ball or bolster and do activities which force the child to participate in crossing of the midline.
- Create a foot maze using masking tape on the floor.
- Jump on trampoline while catching a ball.
- Do animal walks: Donkey Kicks, Pigeon Walks, Bear Crawls, and Duck Walks.
- Jump over a masking tape line or jump rope placed on the floor, using

both feet together. Then jump over a line while standing and landing on the toes of the feet.
- Play Simon Says.
- Complete any activity requiring movement of body in coordinated way.
- Do cross-crawls.
- Do the Hokey Pokey.
- Play Around the World: Sit back to back with another child or adult and pass a ball or small item from one side to the child's other side.

Oculomotor Function

There are sensory diet activities that can be used to improve oculomotor function. Try these ideas:

- Use a scooter board in various activities and games.
- Hit a ball with a bat.
- Toss bean bags into a target with a large arch as the child follows the bean bag with their eyes.
- Create obstacle courses with targets to throw pillows, bean bags, or balls.
- Use a balance board.
- Play on a balance beam.
- Use arrows on the floor to jump in various directions while working on direction change.
- Toss a bean bag in rainbow arc or from one hand to the other and follow the bean bag with the eyes.
- Show the child how to crawl with something on their back while rotating

NEXT PAGE >

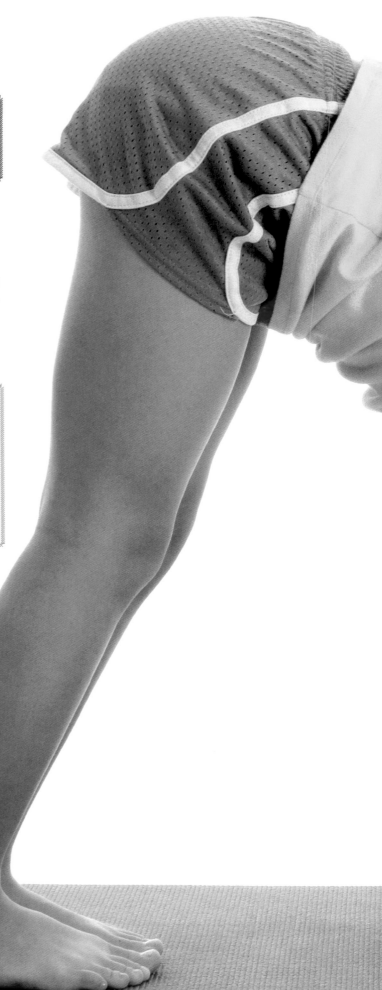

the head from side to side in order to address asymmetric tonic neck reflex integration.

Crossing the Midline

Sensory diet activities can be used to address bilateral coordination and crossing midline. Try these activities:

- Do yoga.
- Catch and throw a ball.
- Complete jumping activities such as jump rope games and jumping jacks.
- Perform Cross Crawls.
- Playing a drum or other instrument.
- Play hand games.

Yoga in a Sensory Diet

Yoga is an activity that addresses many developmental areas. It is a sensory diet tool that can be completed in a group setting in the classroom as a brain break or individually in a child's sensory diet strategy.

Consider all of the benefits of yoga:

* Gross motor strengthening

* Bilateral coordination

* Range of motion

* Core stability and strength

* Crossing midline

* Balance in multiple planes and various positions

* Allows children to understand body awareness

* Uses the entire body

* Teaches children about deep breathing, stretching, and exercise participation

There are yoga poses that incorporate sensory systems such as the proprioceptive and vestibular systems. These are poses that make a great addition to a sensory diet. Yoga positions can be easily incorporated into a themed sensory diet by naming the poses after favorite characters or activities.

Bridge - The child places both feet on the floor, hip width apart. He or she then extends the shoulders back and place both hands on the floor at shoulder width apart. This completes the bridge position. Children can hold the bridge for various lengths. Remind them to keep their head in line with their shoulders and to continue breathing.

Side Plank - The individual positions both feet and arms into a side plank with the legs extended. The hips should be up off the floor and the upper body held up by a flexed elbow. Grade the activity up by asking the child to extend their arm. They can raise the upper arm into the air and hold it as they continue breathing.

Downward Dog - Standing with the feet shoulder width apart, ask the child to place their hands on the floor a few feet in front of their feet.

Cat Pose - The child can position his or her body on all fours with their hands and knees at shoulder and hip width apart. Ask the child to arch and straiten their back as they breathe in and out.

Star - Ask the child to stand with both feet spread beyond shoulder width apart. He or she can bend at the hips and touch the right hand to the left foot and the left hand to the right foot as they breathe deeply.
Hold each position for a count of 10.

Warrior Pose - Ask the child to stand with one foot out in front and the knees slightly bent. Twist at the hips to face front. Ask him or her to extend one hand out in front and to hold one arm extended out behind them. Remind the child to continue deep breaths.

Themed sensory diets for the older child or teen

Older children and students can use themed sensory diets within daily tasks. Many times, teens have interests based on music, characters, books, movies, or other popular theme. Utilize sensory diet strategies based on these topics when possible.

Older children and teens would benefit from many aspects of the sensory strategies listed in this book. Many work and hobby activities can be modified to include calming or alerting sensory input.

Encourage the older child to become more independent in choosing sensory strategies based on their needs. It can be helpful to encourage the older child or teen to identify how their body is responding to sensory input and to utilize a specific set of sensory diet strategies.

Older children will appreciate sensory diet tools such as yoga, deep breathing, meditation, apps, exercise, and jobs that provide heavy work input.

Addendum

Contents:

Sensory-Related Behavior Data Collection Form

DATE AND TIME (When did the behavior occur?)	LOCATION (Where did the behavior occur?)	BEHAVIOR (Describe what happened.)	ANTECEDENT (What happened before the sensory-related behavior?)

Sensory-Related Behavior Data Collection Form

How to use this form:

Parents and teachers can use the first four columns of this form as a screening tool. Therapists and members of the team can use this form as a sheet to recommend sensory strategies and sensory supports related to behaviors. Set a date to follow up and review sensory recommendations. Additional sheets can be used to address different sensory-related behaviors. Behaviors in this book, indicate the manner in which an individual conducts oneself.

1 IDENTIFY THE SENSORY-RELATED BEHAVIOR/S:

Problem behaviors related to sensory regulation needs should be described here. Include context, and resulting responses to behaviors.

IDENTIFY FACTORS CONTRIBUTING TO PROBLEM BEHAVIOR/S:

Use this section to identify contributing factors within the context of the behavior. This can include antecedents to the behavior such as environment, sensory needs, or sensory distractors. This might include sensory input that is needed or sensory input that needs to be reduced/eliminated. Are the behaviors an attempt to gain sensory input or to get away from sensory input? Are attention issues an attempt to get attention or to get away from a task, difficult assignment, or activity? Are self-regulation issues in response to needed self-regulation strategies or as a result of difficulty with responding to specific preliminary events? Be specific in identifying factors contributing to the problem behaviors. Remember that cause/effect factors may not be intentional, and that the underlying sensory components can cause beaviors that may look intentional. Go deep in discovering the "why" behind sensory-related behaviors.

2

Preliminary Events	Setting of Behavior	Describe Behavior	Preferred Behavior	Sensory Strategies Being Used	Sensory Supports (Accommodations/ Modifications) Being Used
Identify specific preliminary events related to a specific behavior incident. Include date and time.	Describe the setting of a specific behavior, including sensory components such as "noisy classroom" etc.	Describe the behavior of the child.	Describe the preferred behavior at this point in the child's environment. Were students to sit quietly at their desks during a video lesson? What was the child expected to do at the time of the behavior?	Indicate current sensory strategies that are being used and the effect of those strategies. Indicate duration, location, and intensity.	Indicate current sensory supports that are in place and indicate the effectiveness of those supports.

3

Completed by/Date: _ _ _ _ _ _ _ _ _ _ _ _ _ _ _ _ _

Sensory Recommendations by/Date: _ _ _ _ _ _ _ _ _ _ _ _ _ _ _ _ _

Follow-up Review: _
_ _

Sensory-Related Behavior Data Collection Form

IDENTIFY THE SENSORY-RELATED BEHAVIOR/S:

IDENTIFY FACTORS CONTRIBUTING TO PROBLEM BEHAVIOR/S:

Preliminary Events	Setting of Behavior	Describe Behavior	Preferred Behavior	Sensory Strategies Being Used	Sensory Supports (Accommodations/ Modifications) Being Used

Completed by/Date: _ _ _ _ _ _ _ _ _ _ _ _ _ _ _ _ _ _

Sensory Recommendations by/Date: _ _ _ _ _ _ _ _ _ _ _ _ _ _ _ _ _ _

Follow-up Review: _

_ _

Sensory Diet Strategy Guide

Behavior/Location:
Sensory Strategy:
Notes:

Behavior/Location:
Sensory Strategy:
Notes:

Behavior/Location:
Sensory Strategy:
Notes:

Behavior/Location:
Sensory Strategy:
Notes:

Behavior/Location:
Sensory Strategy:
Notes:

Behavior/Location:
Sensory Strategy:
Notes:

Behavior/Location:
Sensory Strategy:
Notes:

Behavior/Location:
Sensory Strategy:
Notes:

Sensory Diet Schedule

TIME	ACTIVITY	SPECIAL NOTES:	M	T	W	T	F	S	S

Sensory Diet Effectiveness Tool

	Is there an adverse response to sensory input?
	How does the sensory response present?
	What is the change in reaction following sensory input?
	Does the child experience a change in modulation?
	Does the child appear to exhibit a change in discrimination, regulation, postural control, praxis?
	What does outward behavior look like? Is the child's behavior organized?
	How is the child's self-esteem?
	How long do sensory activities take in order to see a difference in behavior or regulation?
	Are the indicated sensory diet activities effectively carried out by the child's team? Is there an environment where sensory diet activities are not carried through?
	Comments:
	Recommended sensory adjustments:

Daily Sensory Diet Sheet

Date:

⏱ TIME	🏃 SENSORY ACTIVITY	EFFECTIVE? YES/NO	✏ NOTES:

Themed Special Interests Checklist

Use the checklist to identify special themed interests for use in sensory activity planning. Check off the items that are of interest to your child.

CREATING			
☐	Crafts	☐	Setting up pretend scenes
☐	Cutting paper	☐	Building with blocks
☐	Coloring/Scribbling	☐	Playing with play dough
☐	Painting	☐	Folding paper
☐	Art	☐	Tearing paper
☐	Using crayons, markers, pens, pencils	☐	Stapling paper
☐	Drawing	☐	Modeling clay
BUILDING			
☐	LEGOS	☐	Magnaforms
☐	Blocks	☐	Building toys
☐	Tinker toys	☐	Stacking items or toys
☐	Construction toys	☐	
MESSY PLAY / SENSORY PLAY			
☐	Play dough	☐	Finger painting
☐	Slime/goop/oobleck	☐	Soap play
☐	Playing in mud	☐	Lotion
☐	Sticky sensations	☐	Finger nail polish
☐	Sensory play	☐	Bath time
☐	Bare feet in grass	☐	Bubbles
☐	Water play	☐	Playing with bubbles
MUSIC			
☐	Listening to the radio	☐	Playing instruments
☐	Singing	☐	Nursery rhymes
☐	Toys that talk	☐	Church hymns
☐	Microphone toys	☐	Movement songs
☐	Sound books	☐	
SOCIAL INTERACTIONS			
☐	Talking to others	☐	Visiting grandparents/relatives
☐	Listening to others' conversations	☐	Inviting friends over to play
☐	Talking on the phone	☐	Talking on video conference

CARING FOR OTHERS

☐	Dolls	☐	Caring for siblings
☐	Caring for pets	☐	Helping grandparents
☐	Helping others	☐	Telling stories

OUTDOOR PLAY

☐	Being outside	☐	Looking at trees/clouds
☐	Climbing trees	☐	Looking at/for outdoor animals
☐	Playgrounds	☐	Nature walks
☐	Sandbox	☐	Planting/gardening
☐	Pool	☐	Picking flowers
☐	Picking flowers	☐	Going on a sensory walk

MOVEMENT

☐	Running	☐	Sliding
☐	Jumping	☐	Dancing
☐	"Crashing" into cushions	☐	Trampoline
☐	Throwing	☐	Swinging
☐	Car rides	☐	Skipping
☐	Riding in a wagon	☐	Hopping
☐	Rolling	☐	Gymnastics

SPORTS

☐	Throwing and catching balls	☐	Tumbling
☐	Watching sports	☐	Earning points
☐	Playing sports	☐	Team play
☐	Target games (basketball, throwing toys into containers)	☐	Swimming
☐	Wrestling	☐	Gym class

FOOD

☐	Helping prepare meals	☐	Picnics
☐	Setting the table	☐	Baking
☐	Talking about food	☐	Preparing foods for others
☐	Helping with grocery shopping	☐	Looking at cook books
☐	Eating out	☐	Snacks

VEHICLES

☐	Trains	☐	Dump trucks
☐	Trucks	☐	Helicopters

☐	Airplanes		☐	School buses
☐	Cars		☐	Farm vehicles
☐	Construction vehicles		☐	

ANIMALS

☐	Pets		☐	Visiting the pet store
☐	Farm animals		☐	Feeding ducks
☐	Zoo animals		☐	Filling a bird feeder
☐	Insects		☐	Reptiles
☐	Dinosaurs		☐	Birds

SCIENCE

☐	Outer space		☐	Exploring nature
☐	Experiments		☐	Investigating material
☐	Ocean		☐	STEM/STEAM
☐	Reading about science		☐	Mixing "concoctions"

ROCKS / LANDFORMS

☐	Collecting rocks		☐	Sand play
☐	Gemstones		☐	Sorting rocks

PUZZLES

☐	Table-top puzzles		☐	Word searches
☐	Wooden puzzles		☐	Optical illusions
☐	Floor puzzles		☐	Looking at photo albums
☐	Visiting the library		☐	Lift the flap books
☐	Reading books		☐	Series books
☐	I Spy books		☐	Picture books

TECHNOLOGY

☐	Playing on a phone		☐	Hand-held video games
☐	I-pad play		☐	Pokémon
☐	Typing words on a computer		☐	App-type games
☐	Movement video games		☐	

PRETEND

☐	Dolls		☐	Barbie dolls
☐	Stuffed animals		☐	Superheroes
☐	Action figures		☐	Animals
☐	Pretend kitchen		☐	Play phone
☐	Mermaids		☐	Dragons
☐	Unicorns		☐	

OTHER INTERESTS

☐		☐	
☐		☐	
☐		☐	
☐		☐	
☐		☐	
☐		☐	

Sensory Diet Cards

ALERTING SENSORY DIET CARDS

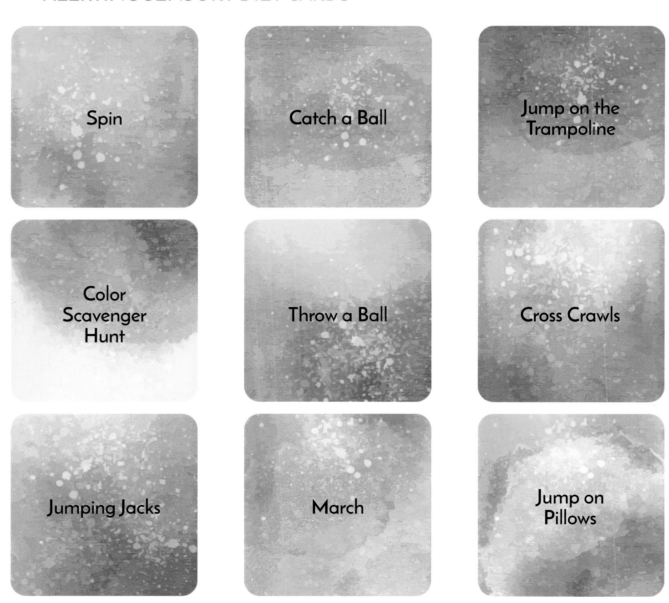

Spin

Catch a Ball

Jump on the Trampoline

Color Scavenger Hunt

Throw a Ball

Cross Crawls

Jumping Jacks

March

Jump on Pillows

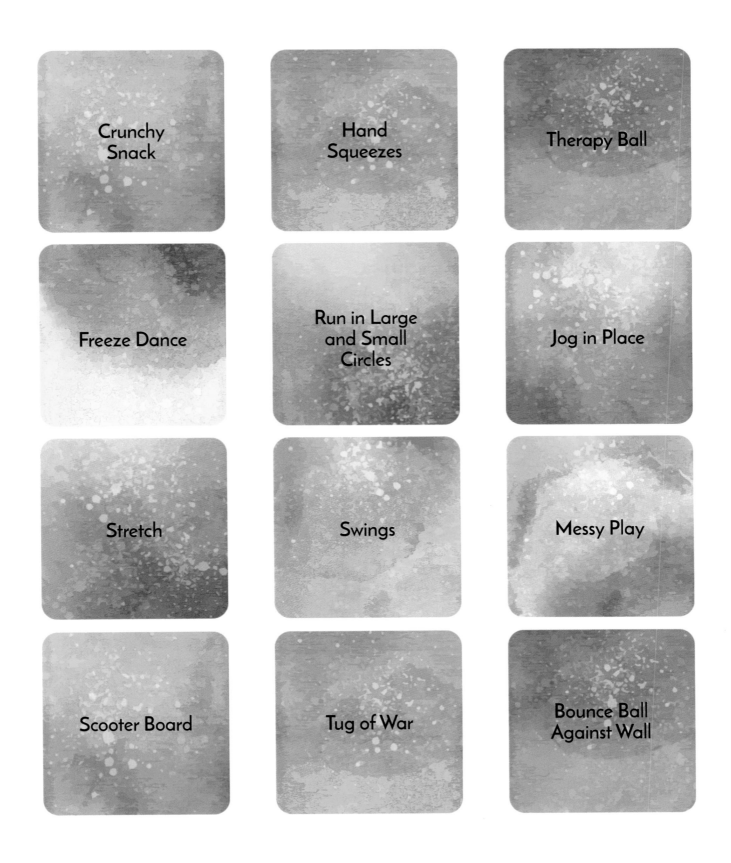

Crunchy
Snack

Hand
Squeezes

Therapy Ball

Freeze Dance

Run in Large
and Small
Circles

Jog in Place

Stretch

Swings

Messy Play

Scooter Board

Tug of War

Bounce Ball
Against Wall

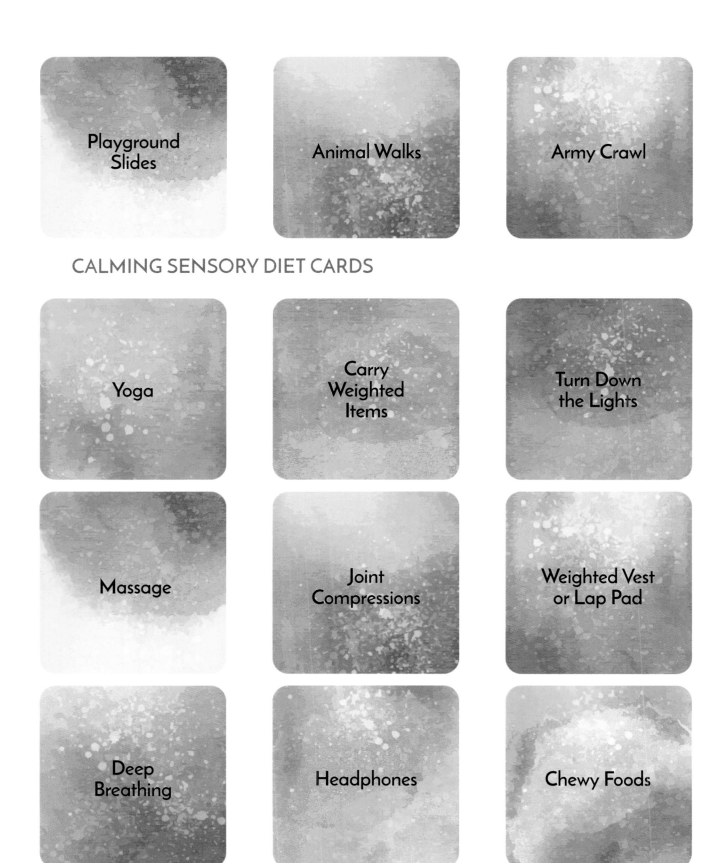

Playground Slides

Animal Walks

Army Crawl

CALMING SENSORY DIET CARDS

Yoga

Carry Weighted Items

Turn Down the Lights

Massage

Joint Compressions

Weighted Vest or Lap Pad

Deep Breathing

Headphones

Chewy Foods

Calm Down Corner

Slow Swinging

Cushion "Sandwich"

Roll Up in a Blanket

Bear Hugs

Weighted Ball

Wall Push-Ups

Drink a Smoothie with a Straw

Hang from Monkey Bars

Calm Down Space

Human "Sandwich" with Couch Cushions

Slow Back Rub

References

- Ayres, A. J., & Robbins, J. (2005). Sensory integration and the child: Understanding hidden sensory challenges. Western Psychological Services.

- Ayres, A.J. (1972). Sensory Integration and Learning Disorders. Los Angeles: Western Psychological Services.

- Fazlioglu, Y., & Baran, G. (2008). A Sensory Integration Therapy Program on Sensory Problems for Children with Autism. Perceptual and Motor Skills, 106, 415–422. Retrieved from: http://dx.doi.org/10.2466/PMS.106.2.415-422.

- Field, T. (1995). Touch in Early Development. Hillsdale, NJ: Lawrence Erlbaum.

- Fisher, A.G., & Bundy, A. C. (1989). Vestibular Stimulation in the Treatment of Postural and Related Disorders. In O.D. Payton, R.P. DiFabio, S.V. Paris, E.J. Protas. & A.G. Van Sant (Eds.), Manual of physical therapy techniques (pp. 239-258). New York: Churchill Livingstone.

- Jones, E., & J. Nimmo. 1994. Emergent curriculum. Washington, DC: NAEYC.

- Koomar, J., & Bundy, A. (1991). The Art and Science of Creating Direct Intervention from Theory. In A. Fisher, E. Murray, & A. Bundy (Eds.), Sensory Integration Theory and Practice (pp. 251–314). Philadelphia: F. A. Davis.

- Mahler, Kelly J., and A. D. Craig. Interoception: The Eighth Sensory System: Practical Solutions for Improving Self-regulation, Self-awareness and Social Understanding of Individuals with Autism Spectrum and Related Disorders. Shawnee Mission, AAPC Publishing, 2016.

- Nackley, V. L (2001). Sensory Diet Applications and Environmental Modifications: A Winning Combination. Sensory Integration Special Interest Section Quarterly, 24, (1) 1-4.

- Precaution. (n.d.). Retrieved January 25, 2018, from https://www.merriam-webster.com/dictionary/precaution

- Thompson, C. J. (2011). Multi-sensory Intervention Observational Research. International Journal of Special Education, 26, 202-214.

- Wilbarger, P. (1995). The sensory diet: Activity programs based on sensory processing theory. Sensory Integration Special Interest Section Newsletter, 18, 1-4.

- Yerxa, E.J., Clark, F., Frank, G., Jackson, J., Parham, D., Pierce, D., Stein, C., & Zemke, R. (1990). An introduction to occupational science: A foundation for occupational therapy in the 21st century. In J. Johnson (Ed) & E.J. Yerxa (Co-eds). Occupational Science: The foundation for new models of practice, (pp. 1 - 17). Binghamton, NY: Haworth Press.

- Woo, C. C., & Leon, M. (2013). Environmental enrichment as an effective treatment for autism: A randomized controlled trial. Behavioral Neuroscience, XX, 1-11. Retrieved from: http://dx.doi.org/10.1037/a00330104.

- Wuang, Y., Wang, C., Huang, M., & Su, C. (2010, April). The effectiveness of simulated developmental horse-riding program in children with autism. Adapted Physical Activity Quarterly, 27, 113-126.

Index

About the Author

Colleen is a registered and licensed Occupational Therapist who graduated from the University of Pittsburgh in 2000. Colleen has worked in a variety of settings as an occupational therapist, including school-based, outpatient pediatrics, acute care, hand therapy, long term care, home care, and skilled rehab. She created and authors the popular occupational therapy website, The OT Toolbox and its corresponding social media outlets. The OT Toolbox website is a valuable resource for therapists, teachers, parents, and anyone who works with the developing child. Colleen strives to share valuable resources related to development through creative activities on the website and social media networks. You can access the therapy tools and resources at www.theottoolbox.com. Colleen has co-authored the popular Functional Skills for Kids books including The Handwriting Book and The Scissor Skills Book, as well as several other multi-author activity books. Colleen resides in Pittsburgh, Pennsylvania with her husband and four amazing children.